Joan Riley was born in Jam
author of four novels, *The*
Twilight (1987), *Romance* (
(1992). Her work has been dramatised for radio and television and widely anthologised in English and in translation. She has taught Literature and Creative Writing and reviewed for a number of publications, including *Africa Concord*, *New Socialist* and BBC World Service. She is currently working on a collection of short stories and a new novel. She lives in London.

Briar Wood was born in New Zealand and grew up in Auckland City. Since coming to Britain in 1983 she has worked as a teacher, critic, editor and writer. She was poetry editor of *City Limits* and has worked as a lecturer in New Literatures in English, Women's Studies and Creative Writing at the University of North London. A selection of her poems were published in *New Women Poets* (Bloodaxe) and *Virago New Poets* (Virago). She returned to New Zealand in 1994 to take up a two year post-doctoral post at Auckland University.

LEAVE TO STAY

Stories of Exile and Belonging

Edited by

Joan Riley and Briar Wood

A *Virago* Book

Published in Great Britain by VIRAGO PRESS 1996

A CIP catalogue record for this book is available from the British Library

ISBN 185381 882 8

Typeset by
Keystroke, Jacaranda Lodge, Wolverhampton

Printed and bound in Great Britain by
Clays Ltd, St Ives plc

Virago
A Division of Little, Brown and Company (UK) Limited
Brettenham House
Lancaster Place
London WC2E 7EN

Contents

Foreword

Where do you open a book for the first time? Where does a book open you? In the middle? Near the end? At a planned or unexpected moment? Do you begin with the list of contents and scan them, looking for a title that has some appeal? Not everyone will turn first to a foreword, so the function of this section isn't only to start the reader off. The Foreword also needs to be like a half-way house, a departure lounge, a hotel or a stop-off point somewhere along the roadside. Since the tracks that criss-cross this anthology touch at so many points around the globe, it seems appropriate that any page might be a launch or a landing site for someone.

The way the representations of imagination and event, microcosm within macrocosm, converge in the pieces selected for *Leave To Stay* is one of the things that makes it a unique, compelling collection. Absorbed though individuals may be in their own narratives, they can find themselves listening to, watching or reading with varying degrees of identification and resistance the monologues, dialogues and polylogues, jokes and asides of fellow travellers. Working as a co-editor was a process of juxtaposing prose and poetry that could convey something of the unexpectedness and complexity of those encounters. Readers have a specific personal and cultural take to add or contrast to the contents of the texts they find here.

My interest in this anthology has developed through a combination of choice and coincidence. Until my early twenties I had never physically travelled outside the South Pacific. Ideas about Britain and North America, which have been formed by the influences of numerous cultures, are constantly transported to and transformed in the structures of the community where I grew up. It can be a humorous, touching, frustrating or even devastating experience to find that moving from one place to another for a significant period involves adjustments to the cultural baggage we all carry with us, however varied it is.

One illustration of how those cultural shifts have stayed with me concerns the London underground. New Zealand has no subway system; I had thought myself familiar with the plan of the underground rail system from a souvenir tea towel, but it took several missed appointments and unplanned city tours before I could read the map adequately for practical purposes. Standing on a platform transfixed with terror as the train hurtled towards me was not the response I had anticipated. The train became an overloaded symbol of all the unspoken fears and estrangements life in an unfamiliar place can hurl towards you, take you away from or leave you stranded with – and that was just a beginning.

There's far more to a word than its roots, but looking back can tell you a lot about thinking forward. The word 'travel' comes from the root 'travail' – to 'labour', 'work', 'toil', 'give birth to', or even 'to put to the torture'. Work and travel as a source of sustenance and pleasure form vital elements in any account of what it is like to become acclimatised to or unsettled by the land- and cityscapes of North America or Britain.

Patterns of travel, settlement, return and departure have long been essential elements of stories and poems. A journey can be circular, triangular, linear; whatever its trajectories it involves an engagement with the shifting boundaries of a contemporary world. No journey can be the same, no reading can be repeated, but there can be confluences, intersections, shared interstices. My hope and belief is that in the course of reading the collection, in whatever order, its itinerant readers will find phrases to remember and writing they will want to return to.

Briar Wood, 1996

Acknowledgements

The editors wish to gratefully acknowledge the following for kind permission to reprint their work:

Kelvin Christopher James, 'Jumping Ship' and 'One Never Knows' from *Jumping Ship and Other Stories* (Villiard Books, 1992); Bapsi Sidhwe, 'Another Golden Opportunity', from *The Crow Eaters* (Jonathan Cape, 1980); Michael Hofmann, 'The Machine That Cried' from *Acrimony* (Faber & Faber, 1986), 'Kurt Schwitters in Lakeland' from *Corona Corona* (Faber & Faber, 1993) and 'Cheltenham'; Zinovy Zinik, 'The White Spring' from *The Mushroom Picker* (Heinemann, 1987) and 'Hooks' from *The New Yorker* (6 November 1989); Hanan Al Shayk, 'I Sweep the Sun off Rooftops' from the book of the same title (Allen & Unwin Australia, 1994); Michael Donoghy, 'A Repertoire' and 'Erratum' from *Erratum* (Oxford University Press, 1993); Sujata Bhatt, 'Walking Across the Brooklyn Bridge' from *Monkey Shadows* (Carcanet, 1993); Joan Riley, 'The Gathering' from *Waiting in the Twilight* (The Women's Press, 1987); Aamer Hussein, 'Letter to Jakarta', an extract from 'Your Children', published in *Mirror to the Sun* (Mantra, 1993); Bharati Mukherjee, 'The Management of Grief' and 'The Tenant' from *The Middleman and Other Stories* (Virago, 1989); Mervyn Morris, 'Checking Out', from *Shadowboxing* (New Beacon, 1979); Mimi Khalvati 'A View of Courtyards', 'Prayer' and

'Coma' from *Mirrorworks* (Carcanet, 1995); Jane Duran, 'Camels', 'Navigator' and 'Braided Rug' from *Breathe Now, Breathe* (Enitharmon, 1995).

Introduction

My grandmother lived in the same house all her life and when she died she was buried in the family plot at the bottom of the yard. Like so many of her generation she never travelled more than forty miles from her birthplace. Her whole world, her hopes, dreams, and preoccupations centred on those forty miles of space.

My mother's generation had larger ambitions and more potential to realise these in the labour shortage of the post-war boom years. They migrated in their tens of thousands from all over the Caribbean, to America, Canada and across the Atlantic Ocean to England with hopes of a bright future for themselves and their children. In England they populated decaying inner cities, replacing earlier migrant and transient populations, injecting the language with their idioms, the landscape with their cultural personalities. In America they carved their own squares in the patchwork of nationalities. Huddling together in little enclaves of familiarity, they took on the ideology and worked hard to achieve a slice of the American dream.

Migration played a large part in my formative years, located as they were in the period of mass emigration from the Caribbean and similar regions. For me the concept became synonymous with economic advancement. I grew up with stories of relatives who had grown rich in England and America. These vivid images of 'rags to riches' were later reinforced by historic ones – European acquisitiveness which devastated the map of the world and brought less ruthless cultures to the brink of extinction, the single largest forced migration that brought my family from Africa to the Americas, Scottish and Irish immigration to the United States in the wake of the Highland clearances and the potato famine.

Mine was a more fortunate experience of migration. Like that of my co-editor Briar Wood it had less to do with economics and more with politics and education. For us it was an easier journey, with a level of privilege and security that few other types of migration enjoy.

Despite this, the experience of being migrant was not an easy one. It was an isolation, being cut off from even the most basic aspects of cultural norms. Everything that had been immutable and unchangeable in our lives was suddenly called into question. It meant painful rethinking of values that had previously appeared universal as they came up against host values of equal strength in both England and the USA. It was a strange reality, a glass bubble existence where having left the comfort and familiarity of homelands there was no easy entry into the host society. This experience forged strange alliances between people with no cultural common ground, but whose shared experience of dislocation created a dialogue of differences and similarities.

As migrants Briar Wood and myself came from worlds as alien to each other as the host space in which we arrived. Our very histories were in conflict, opposite sides of the same colonial coin. She a white New Zealander, I a black Jamaican. What we and other migrants shared was the sense of being misfits, having no personal history within the host country.

It is this odd kinship among the most unlikely fellow travellers that was the impetus for the compilation of this anthology: the sense that one single experience can in some small way transcend different cultures, prejudices and belief systems and create the conditions for a dialogue of space.

This in no way negates the issue of differences, the inequality and injustice based on colour that is so much a part of the dominant ideology in both Europe and America. As an African Jamaican I am as much a target for race hate in England and the

United States as other black people, be they indigenous or migrant. I cannot blend into the landscape. Both societies attempt to polarise, and to reduce me to one-dimensionality, in a way that a white migrant could not understand. At the same time I am as much outsider to the indigenous black people as I am to their white counterparts. I have no shared experience of socialising and schooling. The music I grew up with had a different beat, the landscape a different heat.

The more I considered the phenomenon of migration, the more I realised how commonplace it was. The majority of people in the world have relocated at some point in their lives in contrast to the small distances travelled in my grandmother's time. They have some idea of the strangeness and disorientation resettlement can bring.

To move from one reality to another – even a distance as short as from the English Midlands to London or one state in America to another, from rural to urban or urban to rural – brings new customs, new norms. Things taken for granted in the home space are often viewed as strange or irrelevant in the new place. What is normal and everyday to the incomer can seem suspicious and foreign to the host community. Accents differ, intimate local phrases are unknown and incomprehensible.

If migration across internal distance carries its price, how much worse to migrate from one country to another, changing language, climate, lifestyle, cultural mores, the unspoken exchanges of commonality that aid the transactions of daily life. This was brought forcefully home to me on a journey to a conference in the city of Mannheim. It was by no means my first trip to Germany, but this time the insulation of carefully laid travel plans came apart. Six hours after boarding a train at Frankfurt, a surly conductor informed me we were approaching the Austrian border. Mannheim – a mere hour by train – was now seven hours in the opposite direction. With the illusory security of the small islander I did not check the destination board, no doubt subconsciously expecting the train to stop when it ran out of land. This same illusion has often found me reduced to helpless misery; lost on American interstates or travelling miles in the wrong direction in British trains. On a small island you eventually come to the sea; for me as an islander a continent is an incalculable distance.

Stranded on a platform in a small German town, unpronounceable to my clumsy foreign tongue, I was reduced to a vocabulary of fewer than a hundred words – many of them useless questions about family, relationships and restaurant menu items. The myth that all Germans spoke English evaporated after my umpteenth attempt at communication exhausted my five usable sentences of the language. It brought back the initial sense of being overwhelmed, dwarfed, regressed and bewildered I experienced in both England and America, until my eyes adjusted to those landscapes. Two white American soldiers boarded the train for the return trip to Frankfurt. I still remember the sense of relief at the sound of English-speaking voices. All my prejudices against American militarism, racism, consumerism and the other pigeon-holding labels were suspended at the familiar sense of foreign incomprehensibility in the face of local certainties. I had a lot of time to ponder the difference between media-defined images of migration and the reality. To think too of the contrasting realities of the two countries where I have spent significant time.

In Britain I have made lasting connections. I have a fondness for London in much the way I am fascinated by New York. Different cities, worlds apart. One aggressively modern, grid built, a brash statement against the skyline. The other a twisted, tangled, idiosyncratic jumble of old and new. Yet each giving the same sense of standing at one of the main confluences in the world.

A writer whose work appears in this collection calls London '*the place where someone from everywhere in the world finally comes*'. I feel the same way about New York. I fancy if I stand still long enough in Times Square I will meet someone from every corner of the earth. Each of us will have similar feelings and experiences, be we transient or migrant, translated into endless differences by personal and cultural histories. Yet these similarities and differences, so much a part of writers as diverse as Bapsi Sidhwe, Zinovy Zinik, Yasmin Issacs, Michael Donoghy, Hanan Al Shayk – even Briar Wood and myself as editors originating a world away from each other – have never formed a sustained part of literary debate.

As an adult my images of migration are far removed from my childhood and adolescent concepts. Gone are the naive ideas of rags to riches or the simplistic anger at European exploitation. Surprisingly, the most powerful replacements are not from personal experience but are the famous images that are as much icons as pop art and postmodernism. My montage includes the plight of the war refugees, the old flickering footages of the *Empire Windrush* bringing surplus labour from the 'West Indies'. Ships from behind the Iron Curtain, full to overflowing, human barnacles clinging to every handhold as they flee the waning star of the Communist East. Desperate faces crowded against the wire mesh of internment gazing at the illusion of freedom on the other side. Boat people huddling desperately in flimsy crafts, clinging to rafts of inner tyres, defying nature. Other containers, bobbing between sea and sky, ominously empty underline the treacherous reality of shark-infested coral seas. These are images on a heroic scale, tragedy so great they shrivel and eclipse the individual till they become lost in the vastness of scale.

Alongside were the images of literature. The artist as romantic or wandering Bohemian, eternal exile making impartial critical commentary on the contradiction and frailties of social living, cast adrift with no place of ownership. Migration itself had become a cliché.

As editors we made a conscious decision against the familiar 'experts' in migrant writing when putting together this anthology. Instead we sought a mix of experiences, writers who could focus on the prosaic and the ordinary as well as the pathos and the pain of making sense of new realities. We were aware that this would create a tension between the text and the commercial necessities of the market-place. After all, the world of the book publisher, seller and newspaper critic is divided into neatly labelled slots.

The texts in print most often fragment the migrant experience into artificial, usually exotic, shapes to satisfy expectations. Anthologies tend to cover particular racial, cultural or gender groupings and give a detached panoramic commentary on host countries or nostalgic long-range exploration of homelands.

In contrast, individuals have been able to use their migration as an active shaper in their awareness of differences. These perceptions have brought new interpretations to the English and American landscape; edges of uncertainty which pull apart and reinvent realities. Incomer and host rub against each other, eroding lines of certainties, the surface negative of perceptions disguising vitality and creativity like sand grains in an oyster shell.

We were acutely aware of the differences between the United States and Britain: one a patchwork quilt, flavoured a little by every place on earth, its constantly evolving urban spaces and fascination with external realities forging a contrast of the new with a hunger for the old; the other, very much the old – grand, decaying, eccentric, secretive and seedy.

We decided on a thematic framework in an attempt to tease out some of the areas of differences and similarities between people and places. We offered the contributors specific headings designed to look at seven areas of life through the eyes of the writer as migrant from the point of entry to exit or accommodation. This approach has put together contributions of contrasting flavours which at times have surprising echoes of the same preoccupations. 'Jumping Ship,' Kelvin Christopher James's tale of unconventional entry to America, focuses on a New York of risks and possibilities that finds uneasy comparisons in the loss of hope and morality which befalls Pierre Tran's character in 'The Deal', set in the Wall Street world of blank glass buildings and high finance. In 'From a Diary' Adam Lively's diarist captures the sheer scale and beauty of the dwarfing and exhilarating Oregon landscapes where small intimate detail brings focus to the vastness of the whole, while Sujata Bhatt views a whole world in 'Walking Across the Brooklyn Bridge'.

Across the water there is a different scale of vista. Hanan Al Shayk's 'I Sweep The Sun off Rooftops' and Yasmin Issacs's haunting poem of disintegration 'Some Say it's Madness' rip open the myth of London to expose a fascinating and uncomfortable underside. Jan Lo Shinebourne's story 'Oh Buddha' which centres on a woman's attempts to get therapy, explores the uneasy, mismatched edges of host culture and incomer with a warm and irresistible humour. Aamer Hussein's 'Sweet Rice' explores the loss of role and the resultant compressed reality faced by a professional woman whose qualifications are not recognised in Britain, while Zinovy Zinik's 'Hooks' raises questions of relationships with both host space and homelands. Themes of loss and hope recur time and again in different guises, along with the multi-layered nature of displacement.

As editors we saw every part of being migrant as the vehicle of many stories. Arrival with all its connotations of journey's end and new beginnings, yields to other stories as we settle in and start on the road of new realities, picking up the ordinary threads of life – school, higher education, work, parenting; making new connections, renegotiating relationships with the family and friends left behind in the old country. Moving through sickness and good health in a strange place and reaching a *point* of accommodation with the new country, a move to another one or a return to the homeland.

We did not set out to create a definitive or expert text, but to capture some of the contradictions that exist within the parameters of migration. We deliberately asked the writer, as migrant, to write about the day-to-day issues of living in a foreign space. We hoped this would offer a dialogue peculiar to itself. That the uniqueness of perceptions, through different cultural languages, different norms and expectations, different genders and family histories, would create a dynamic interchange.

Leave To Stay is lively, energetic, and above all unpredictable. The discomfort of dislocation is at once poignant, humorous, irreverent and deeply significant. Hints of nostalgia edge the substance of the real. We have a strong sense of writers looking at themselves among others; bringing their cultural baggage but using it skilfully to negotiate the foreign space. No two writers have the same cultural perspective. Each story or poem is unique, yet each holds common threads of dislocation and displacement without being self-indulgent or condemning.

Joan Riley, 1996

Crash Pad

Briar Wood

Joining a Nothing To Declare queue,
the suitcase tied with baling twine
spilt open –
A Keuchenhof of springsummer things.
Dropped like flotsam
from the stratosphere's
all clear
to the tartan of Heathrow fields.

Have *I* the right to remain silent?

Stranded on the landing
among rucksacks
Five to a room.
An Earl's Court Bed and Breakfast.
That barmaid faking orgasm to the tune of
I Come from the Land Down Under.

That body in the alleyway
with multiple gunshot wounds.
Headlines making Drug Connections.
Clapped out camper vans
the police ask them to move on.

Haven.
A place off Ladbroke Grove.
Four floors round the rackety stairway.
No fire escape.
A lawnmower bulldogs the door.
Whose flat is this anyway?
Someone's cousin's.

Lukewarm tea free at Latymer Road
  Christian Centre.
Sin Now, Pay Later.
The writing on the wall advises.
It is nineteen eighty-four.
And Doublespeak means
whatever Mrs Thatcher says goes.

Trawling the supermarket
for cartons of Kia Ora –
fruit juice that tastes like silage.
Kiwi polish.
Anchor. (To keep up the butterfat content.)

At a phone booth
the soon-to-be-privatized British Telecom
overlooked,
You can call anywhere in the world for zilch.
Straggling afterwork line-ups
nearly circling the block
at Hackney.

Ingrid I say Ingrid
Remember the Russian Novel Phenomenon.
Guess who this is?
Yeah she says it's half past two
in Geraldton.
The baby has just gone to sleep.

Sade's Smooth Operator
echoing from the headset of a Walkman
clamped to the ear
The sea thundering in its shell.
Heatwaves
smashing through a window.

Pub crawlers get raucous.
The receiver's off the hook.
A voice saying huskily
She nearly blew me out.
It was touch and go.
James telling anybody
the one about the insomniac dyslexic.

I lie awake at three thirty-six
wondering if there is a dog.
Chorusing snores.
Sheepskin slipper tiptoes across an Arctic camp.
The lounge by night.
A flotilla of lilos.

Waking up to cramp,
one arm numb as a pincushion.
Stilted morning saunters.
Eyes like road maps.
Kangat and Oxyacetylene
blasts from Ma Vlast.

The wardrobe's jumble of cast-offs.
Dew damp swandris.
A present of Manuka honey
from those who try going home to Paeroa
or leave for Pamplona
and don't come back.

Jumping Ship

Kelvin Christopher James

Bountin sat on the foredeck grinding teeth into his frustration. His eyes were fixed on the steamer's tie ropes as they sagged and tautened with the rhythm of the swells. They swayed a patient beat of tide rising, of sun going down. Of time moving as it would. Moving, and leaving Bountin stranded. The long summer day was moving on, and he wasn't. Binding him on this steamer's deck was his partner, him sitting over-shoulder behind on a bale of rope: Ruinsey, his friend, a man treating Opportunity like a slave.

Bountin, for one, never took on this last three weeks of stevedoring up the Gulf Stream to end it sitting on deck taking in orange-coloured sun rays. That was never the why he had ridden this seasickening steel bridge across the ocean. He, for one, had come here to get in the solid Land of Plenty.

Yet, for more than an hour now, he had been watching other ship workers filing down the gangplank, all just walking off and up the pier. Among them were some he suspected of having travel arrangements just like his. And none of his suspects had returned. So it seemed the gate into the place was working. And all Bountin wanted to know was why they, too, weren't trying it.

Bountin's generous resolve to bear up in silence slackened under this assault of reasonableness. He heaved a deep sigh, and his independent head twisted towards where Ruinsey was comfortable. Before he could complete his glance, though, Ruinsey hawked and spat a pellet between them; cleanly clearing the ship's rail six feet away, it seemed to banner rebuke in its comet's tail, making Bountin wrench his guilty attention back to the ropes. Although now the grind of his teeth could've crunched diamonds, and the response in his mind was, 'Why y'don't spit up your stagnant backside?'

For the *n*th time, Bountin's eyes, restless as the sea gulls gliding above him, roved to midships where the gangplank joined ship to shore – his gangway into the American port city . . . A swift tension ballooned within him. To stifle it, he forced a deep draught of the damp sea air, and at the back of his nose, the tension found a taste: a foreign tang suggesting machined air. The sort of taste action would have . . .

Still, he refused to ask the question eating him, shy to because, in truth, the whole venture – the scheming, arranging, all and else – did belong to Ruinsey; Bountin himself being along for company, and to seek his own luck. With this thought, he shy-eyed at his partner with fresh indulgence, and tried harder to deal with the creeping time. For here he was, at the end of that master of a move: he country-wild and Caribbeano, jumping ship into America . . .

That they were so close! A thrill seized him, shivering across his back and chest, crawling like ants about his balls. He almost jumped to his feet, but caught himself. Instead, he tensed and stretched – his legs, his arms, his back – then yawned extra wide like the wakeful lion.

A hailing voice provided a distraction: 'Yow, Coconut! Ain'tcha goin' t'town? Afraid to lose yer monkey ass, huh?' The taunt ended with its owner's laughter, like a jackass braying after it had farted.

It came from a chubby brown-skinned fellow Ruinsey called 'Flabber'. He was an American, the ship's cook. He had decided that, of all the Caribbeanos in the crew, Ruinsey was to be jape's stock on the menu for the three-week freight run. So, at chow time in the galley, it was Ruinsey he pestered with 'Coconut' and 'Monkey' nicknames. Other Bloods wore hair in braids, or natural locks; yet it was Ruinsey's tresses that suggested 'Golliwog' and 'Snakehead' to Flabber. Every time they went to eat, Flabber became the pesky mosquito: bites and buzzings and all.

And what had Ruinsey done about all this? Nothing but play the statue. As if he didn't see, or hear, or feel. He just sat and listened. Still, on good sea days, when they were eating topsides, he would calm down Bountin's yearning to revenge him. 'Man, I have a plan,' he'd say. 'Every fatted hog got his Saturday, and Flabber day is coming.'

Now Flabber swaggered down the gangplank and, not satisfied with his joke, turned at the bottom and made an ugly face at them. Then he shouted something else. But the distance, and the gulls' cries, and the breeze, took it.

'Fuck you, Fat Lips!' Bountin screamed back, maybe in vain, as Flabber began striding away up the long pier into America.

When Bountin turned around, though, Ruinsey had stood up. His beat-up leather bag was swung ready over his shoulder. And in a flash the answer snapped into Bountin's head. That was why they had been waiting! Grinning with his insight, he gleamed a look in Flabber's direction. But the target was already gone, lost in the eight o'clock waning of the long and tired day.

Eyes full on him, Ruinsey cocked his head and asked, 'You understanding now?'

Bountin nearly answered the lie that he had divined the plan years ago. Instead, being easy, he said, 'Yeah, yeah, yeah.'

And not wanting the lesson that might follow, he looked away – toward the narrow, sloping gangplank inviting them down. 'So . . . we going now, right?' he said.

'Unless y'don't want catch-up to catch him!' Ruinsey answered.

For Bountin, the gangplank was no real necessity. His anticipation alone could've shot him across the space from rail to pier; he could've sprung up and glided over, like those after-hours gulls. But he was with Ruinsey, on his mission. So Bountin merely slapped at whatever might've stuck to his pants' seat. Then he bounced off.

All the walk up the long pier, Bountin stoppered his excitement and refrained from asking Ruinsey his intent for Flabber. He was still trying to determine it by himself when a chain-link fence surprised up out of the evening. He looked it over: where the lock was, the clearance at the bottom, the barbed overhang at the top. A sudden banging interrupted from his left. They turned and saw the window half of the sentry-hut door opening. A head with a guard's cap poked out and sounded a bleat in nasal pitch, like a goat enquiring after grass. There was a pause.

Bountin looked sharply at Ruinsey, fishing for a clue, or a signal. Ruinsey was staring at the man from eyes edged with blankness. Then his eyes turned to the gate, as if it could offer help, or translation. Bountin fixed on the gate also, now measuring its height, the size of the links, about how many steps it'd take to climb over.

The guard broke the silence. With the same accent, but slower, he said all in one, 'Say!-y'all-speak-English-or-what? Habla-say-Español? Eh! ¿Qué-bota?'

Ruinsey cleared his throat, said, 'Cargo vessel, *Flying Jenny*. Shore leave . . . '

His voice, sounding a little higher than usual, stopped short, interrupted by a purposeful buzzing, which continued long enough, as the guard pulled his head back in like a turtle. The window slid shut – *Thumptt!!!*

Nothing else happened. Checking Ruinsey for understanding, Bountin found Ruinsey checking him.

Vluuppt!!! The window slid open again. The guard's head popped back out. Glaring, grimacing, it jerked at the fence, 'Get-da-gawddamn-gate!' it snarled.

The fed-up head disappeared. And the buzzing began again. It sounded more riled-up.

This time they both started fast for the gate, which, as it was pushed upon, clicked open and let them, easy so, into the paradise, America.

Their first scene was a long, wide, empty highway disappearing streetlight by streetlight into the darkness.

Bountin took it all in, looking about for some signs of life: for people, a car, anything. He expected more. Just what, he didn't know. He had this zest to shout at somebody. Or throw a stick. Or say 'Hiya!' Yankee-style.

Ruinsey caught his arm roughly. 'First thing is, we have to make Flabber remember. Right?'

Bountin came down to earth. He nodded, looked along both ends of the disappearing street, and asked, 'Y'know which way he went?'

Ruinsey pointed to the left, a bit up beyond the streetlights. 'That glow over there is the shining city. That's where he gone. And no car passing here this hour. So he gone walking.'

It was such common sense, Bountin knew he could've figured it out also. He just hadn't known how high to look, or how to read what he saw. And all that was the stuff Ruinsey taught him. Every day, past and now.

On impulse he grabbed Ruinsey's arm and stopped him soft eye to hard. Then he had so much thanks to say, he told him only, 'Ruinsey, mi' man, this place ent so hard.'

Ruinsey looked at him queerly and broke out his full smile that disappeared his eyes into wrinkles.

'I knew you'd like it, man. From the *f* in first, I knew it.'

All their back-slapping dislodged the bag from Ruinsey's shoulder. And, as if that had knifed his mood, his grin turned down grim. 'But I don't want to feel good yet, man,' he said, then looked up the road to the city lights where Flabber was heading.

Bountin said eagerly, 'Ay! man, I'm ready like Freddy.' He recalled all the times Flabber had played the nettle for his man, and raked and stirred these angers into the working rage that'd drive him now to sting back. For yes! prickle cutting-down time was come.

Ruinsey adjusted his bag so it hung on his back. Then, muttering, 'Now for his ass . . . ' he set off at a brisk lope, Bountin easy at his side.

At first sight of him, they crossed from the far side of the overwide double street. Directly behind him then, they closed in with silence more than speed. Until, with a pouncing spurt, they were upon Flabber. Bountin kicked him behind the knees into a crouch, while Ruinsey caught him in a choke hold and wrestled him down to the edge of the sidewalk, crushing his face into the scrawny grass. So the first idea Flabber had of something happening was when he tried to scream. But his voice caught on too high and failed, and by then he lost his wind to a gargle. For with a pull, a rip, and a tug over, Ruinsey'd covered Flabber's head with his own denim jacket, leaving him well trussed up. Just for something more to do, Bountin kneed Flabber in the ribs, making him squeal and choke out, 'Oh God! Oh God! Don't kill me . . . '

Meantime, Ruinsey drew his gilpin: it with an edge like a new toothache. He, eyeing Bountin with silent strategy as he pulled it out. Bountin caught his design in an instant, and they changed holding positions slightly, allowing easier breathing for Flabber.

Thus he was begging for mercy more plainly when Ruinsey made his strike. As the blade sliced across his seat, a spitty wheezing joined with Flabber's cry, blending into an indrawn whimper, softer than the whisper of his splitting seating layers: the jeans blue one, the white shorts one, then the skin itself – a lighter brown than expected, and innermost, a pale, pink flesh springing tiny drops of blood that quickly flooded down the new-cut crevasse.

Henceforth, Flabber'd know stretching pains each time he stooped to shit. Good vengeance, since it was relieving his other hole that had brought this on. Bountin grinned at the logic of it as Ruinsey spat finally on his cringing victim. Then they walked off to the city, leaving him huddled and blabbering there.

*

They took a few false turns around long, wasteland blocks before they got near the source of the glowing. Then they could see headlamps flashing by cross streets not far in front of them. Here they paused to set themselves: to resettle the clothes on the body, to gather an easy pose for walking, to ready their eyes in their faces. Then, when they felt right, they walked up to the next intersection and turned into the flow of the actual, living American street.

'This must be a main avenue . . . ' Ruinsey kept repeating softly, more to himself.

Bountin had no contention with that, or anything else. He was taking in the lights. The so many lights everywhere he gazed with bedazzled eyes. Not only sizes, but every shape! and colour. Blinking and flashing. Action lights. Sliding along picture advertisements. Popping on, emptying off. Pairing up in beams on shining cars, going and coming, red and brilliant. Shimmering the streets into golden streams, and rippled silver, and weird glitters, and hanging-tree shadows from the looming goose-necked lamp poles; lamp poles tall and aloof as royal palms.

Several times Bountin stared himself into collisions: with people, poles, poodly dogs, and potholes. After enduring some verbal abuse and vague pain, he marshalled his attention to immediate focus on the people flowing beside and about him like river sands eddying. They passed in multitudes of vital, plain, and regular sorts. Many carried a flair. Regardless of how it came out, they tried for a difference, in clothes, or makeup, or walking stride. No one seemed to care when the gimmick didn't work. No jibes, no embarrassment, even if frogface wearing silks was escorting pussycat in satin. Everybody was full of themselves, going along intent, overlooking any disturbance that'd vary their own destinations. Bountin marvelled. This was all right!

A girl coming past him was wearing cutoffs that never stopped. Just loudly enough he hailed her, 'Hey, Sugar Juice!'

She caught the pass, together with his bold eye. Bold right

back, she smiled full and close at him, then mouthed him a kiss as they passed each other forever, indulging him a lasting moment of honey. Hers was the City's welcoming kiss. It said he was among his kind of people. He was in his native place . . .

Ruinsey's voice nudged into his attention, insistent about transport they needed to find, some 'subway' train to get them to his contact in the city, to some woman expecting them.

Bountin waved an arm at his bothering, indicating the scene about them. 'Which city? This isn't the city?' he asked.

Ruinsey let the question rise into the night. He only muttered, 'Well . . . ' and turned to searching through his bag, from which he took a notebook page and read it with many puzzled looks, as if the words were making strange signs at him.

'This could be any part of it. Look, man! I never been here, y'know . . . ' Ruinsey stopped, hmmm'd like a lawyer, then went on, 'Listen! These directions say we *have* to get a subway . . . whatever it is.'

Bountin couldn't figure why Ruinsey sounded so concerned. Finding the train couldn't be that difficult. It was a public vehicle. They just had to ask somebody, and he, for one, wasn't shy. And even if they missed the train, he was sure they could walk to Ruinsey's contact. It was one city, after all. They had all night, and he wasn't tired.

'You want me to find out from that papers man over there?' Bountin asked.

Ruinsey shrugged okay, and handed over the paper. Then he added, 'But don't make show of yourself too much, eh? We've got to be inconspicuous. You understand?' His forehead was all frowned up in anxious ditches as he spoke, his eyes red with trouble lines.

All his show of dread was only firing up Bountin's temper. Why all this advice and concern? How come suddenly he was a cross to Ruinsey's shoulder?

'Since when you so worried about me?' he demanded, unable to keep the sarcasm and heat out of his voice. 'You don't think your partner could handle, eh? Tell me!'

But he didn't wait for Ruinsey's answer. Didn't want one. The question was his point. He just stalked off to the newspaper stand.

With his partner's misgivings policing his mind, Bountin was strict on his politeness. He waited until the man was free, then said, 'Good night, mister.'

When nothing happened, he repeated it louder, twice.

Finally, the man looked at him and said, 'Yeah, what?'

'Can you direct me to the train? Please.'

'Which 'un?'

'The subway one . . . '

'Yeah, yeah. Which 'un?'

Bountin looked him over and saw the man was serious. So he tried, 'Any one going in the city.'

'Better y'take the bus,' the man said. 'Stops one block over.'

Bountin leaned his elbows on the counter, and struck a pondering pose. He shook his head. 'No, I want to catch the train.'

'Same token,' the man answered.

Bountin couldn't follow this meaning. So he remained the thoughtful one; began turning about the note he held and looking at it as if *it* had failed to satisfy.

The man took the hint. 'Here, let's see that!' he said, and reached over his counter and plucked the note away. He waved it to arm's length and squint-focused to read. Then he returned it to Bountin.

'You'd be better off with th' bus,' he said. 'Your train's way 'cross town.'

Bountin kept his pose; added a this-is-great-news smile. 'Yes? Which direction?'

He spoke with much marvelling in his tones. The man pointed. Bountin nodded as if heady with a privilege. Then, as if afterthinking, he asked, 'So, how far is 'cross town?'

The man looked at him curiously, grimaced a clown mouth, fingering down the ends while he considered. 'Thirty, maybe forty blocks,' he said.

Bountin smiled at him, straightened up, and put the directions in his pocket. Before he walked away, he said, 'Thank you for your kindness, mister.'

The man called after him, 'Y'should take th' bus . . . same token.'

Bountin, feeling champion, dashed into the street, noticed the red DON'T WALK while lithely skipping through some braking traffic towards the other side of the road. His satisfaction would've been really complete if Ruinsey had witnessed his handling the man. That certainly would've finished all the anxious nonsense in his mind: that Bountin had lost his touch.

The man had pointed back along the way they had come. So they crossed a broad, busy one-way street, and went. Right away Bountin became spellbound by the lights again, all so close around from lamp pole to ground levels, while straight up above was opaque blackness. It was all upside down: as if the sky had upended its contents all around them, transforming the people, the stores, even the plain concrete he walked. The scattering star-fall had drenched the street with sparkle and changed the place into a bustle of glaze and glitter.

A glance at his partner striding alongside made Bountin realise that Ruinsey hadn't been sparking at all. Much more than his fashion, he had gone silent. Bountin began worrying for explanation. About Flabber? Not likely. They had done a good revenge – not even the victim was witness. In any case, Ruinsey never took on that sort of problem. His motto was 'Make life simple, take it as it comes.'

It occurred to him that Ruinsey might be tired. Or hungry. That just might be it. He himself, on thinking, was middling peckish.

'You slowing down, or what? How you so quiet?' he asked.

Ruinsey acknowledged him only a distracted, no-comment look.

They were coming up to a one-door store whose neatly laden stalls encroached halfway across the sidewalk. Pyramids of citrus, apples, bananas, mangoes, and other fruits competed colourfully for attention. Inspired, Bountin approached quickly, as he said to Ruinsey, 'Man, what you need is some vitamins.'

And with that, he crouched over the banana stall, and swiftly slipped a yellow-ripe hand into his shirt's bosom. Then, with a big grin, he sped off, surging through the sidewalk's throng, casting backwards looks.

It was a couple of moments before he realised there was no pursuit. No one had come out of the store to throw even a look at him. So he slowed down to the pace of the crowd, which had just so calmly accepted all his shoving and rushing through. Finally, he stepped off the curb between two parked cars and waited for Ruinsey to catch up. The incurious crowd went by as if he weren't there. So he broke out a banana to munch while his partner arrived. And when he did, fell into step beside him, and offered him some food.

As if taking example from Ruinsey, the street was becoming quieter. The several past blocks carried less and less traffic: people, business, and otherwise. Bountin commented on this.

'It must be getting late,' was all Ruinsey said.

Being patient with the man's mood, Bountin let that comment remain where it dropped. He himself hadn't been thinking of time, but of how the quiet streets seemed relieved, and freer in the more space they now had. And about how the air even had a lighter smell. And how the soft slap of the tossed banana peelings carried truer. And how he felt betting certain it was easier now to jump higher, or explode a lungful in a shout. But Bountin didn't bother bringing up all this. Not to a Ruinsey seeing the night only as a clockface.

—

It was a dimly lit, vertical sign placed abruptly next to some stairs leading underground. Involved with the rhythm of walking blocks and crossing streets, they nearly missed it. Seeing the stairs, right away Bountin realised that 'subway' meant underground railway system, and with more excitement, that the trains ran through tunnels in the earth. That idea made him laugh out loud. He clapped Ruinsey's shoulder. 'Y'see that, Ruinsey? And I was looking for a railway station, y'know, the water tanks, a platform, a signalman. Y'following me?'

Ruinsey nodded understanding, but didn't talk. Although, from the way his front foot was groping for the first tread, Ruinsey, too, had to be getting impressed right past his popping eyeballs.

Halfway down, at the zig in the zigzag staircase, Ruinsey took a packet of slugs from his bag. They were ten tokens, he said. Bought from his contact man on the cargoship, they were part of the stowaway job package. He handed five to Bountin.

'I hope these tokens working for this train, y'know,' Ruinsey said, worried.

Bountin considered this. 'Well, that ent the worst,' he said. 'If they don't work, we could just jump over. That turnstile ent a good three feet.'

Ruinsey looked him over a long one. Then he said, 'Bountin, you must stop thinking that way now. Okay? You not home. This is America. We can't be drawing attention so, or they will catch we. You have to calm down, man.'

Ruinsey was being so solemn, Bountin made a check-up grin at him. 'But how you so serious, Ruinsey? You sermonising in paradise, man. I was only making joke. I know we not jumping.'

Ruinsey didn't acknowledge him. Instead, back stiffened, token in hand, he led off for the turnstile. They put their tokens in the slots, and they worked just fine.

The underworld train ride was the final gate through which the City stormed to possess Bountin. Its assault began immediately, as with hurricane roaring, a one-eyed dragon-monster filled the tunnel, rushing up to them. Then, with a great shrieking, it turned out to be their grumbling train, restrained and shuddering, but, unnaturally, blowing steam nowhere. No sooner had it stopped than side panels scraped open and people tumbled out like finished batches. Doing as others who had waited, Ruinsey and he pushed into the carriage against the out-flow. Then, inside, propped on hard, plastic seats, they watched the doors guillotine shut, and with a jolt, they were fast off, shrieking like a cross dragon again. But now inside it.

Under mountains? Under rivers? From what Bountin could make out of their passage, it could've been anywhere. Outside the row windows, the carriage's lights reflected off whizzing walls and sudden poles, where the checkered patterns of light strung into speeding bullets that disappeared for dark moments before returning to dazzle. All this was close to hypnotising him when another charging rumble *vroomph*ed by, going the other way, and shattered his trance with a fist of sound force.

Bountin palmed away a slack feeling from his face. The dripping sweat was one thing; the bigger bother was a glazed view he tried squinting away. Yet it still seemed they were inside a bolt of lava, hurtling through the earth, aiming for eruption at some volcano, somewhere and soon. And very powerful they were; very dangerous, too. He had this sense that, although his feet were standing still, they were really flying, skimming over ground. One supporting proof was the wheel-whirring in his soles, which was also vibrating through his seat, and setting an annoying edge to his teeth. He stood up abruptly to change the pressures, and the annoying thrilling stopped; but on standing, he was unbalanced and almost fell. He only saved himself by an instinctive snatch overhead, where his hand found a securing hook. It was so exactly in the right place that Bountin realised it must have been put there for just that convenience. To him, it was such a practical forethought that he hung his head down close to Ruinsey's to speak his admiration for the designers.

'Isn't this something else again? . . . ' he began, and couldn't hear himself above the train's roar. So he cleared his throat for the challenge, and shouted, 'Ruinsey, isn't this something?'

As if Bountin's shout had caught him in a mean dream, Ruinsey jerked up, aggressive with alarm, asking, 'What!!! What!!!'

This startled, fighting readiness put Bountin off his cheery mood. He was about to scream, 'Forget it!' But right then his throat broke into a coughing fit from strain. And he could only hang there from the handhold, and rack his belly bones narrow with spasm after weakening spasm.

Meanwhile, Ruinsey kept repeating, 'Calm down, man, you have to take it easy . . . ' as if it were mischief Bountin was making. As the seizure passed, Bountin felt the train slowing down. So he sat down to compose himself.

The door panels crashed open. Some people got up and hustled out. One or two rushed in as if under catch-up pressures. Then, through the door right in front of him, three guys dressed up female sauntered into the carriage ever so coolly, as if they never noticed how the gates just missed smashing their shitting ends into skinny streaks. With lots of chichi and wiggling, they teetered their high heels to the plastic bench and sat primly, as if cautious of their hard ends testing against the plastic hardness.

Bountin was never so astonished. They were so weird, and so comfortable at it, he couldn't believe their boldness. He wondered at them, amazed. Did they never pass mirrors? Had they no family, or caring friends, to advise them of their appearance? Of their makeup caking between sprouting moustache hairs, of those muscled hairy calves, of those high-coloured, pointed-heel size fifteens. How could these guys stand up anywhere in public? Had they hidden in the toilet to wait for this train? Suddenly amused, Bountin decided these guys truly deserved a 'Big-Balls Boldness' trophy. For with their display of gumption, they had to be carrying at least four sets of the daringest miracles ever.

The perspiration-moustache one stared back at Bountin. 'What's your problem?' he asked in girlish tones.

Bountin could hold it in no more. He burst out laughing, weakening himself so, he leaned on Ruinsey for support.

'How quaint,' commented the eye-shadowed one with scarlet lips, then closed heads with the others for a giggle chorus.

Ruinsey eased Bountin off as if he didn't know him. 'Take it easy, man,' he muttered.

Right away a part of Bountin's mind raged, *Take what easy?* But he was still laughing in part also. Only now there was nothing funny to his mirth. He just continued with the noisy grimacing from spite.

The plucked-eyebrows one was now staring him down. Then he proceeded to japing with flirting blinks, and moues, and tossing head. Bountin sprang up and stood over him. 'You like me, Horse-mouth?' he challenged. 'You want mih cock? Y'want it crowing in your face, eh?'

He hefted his crotch in Plucked Eyebrows' face, who pulled back and ladied, 'What is your problem, sir?'

'I don't have none, you no-cunt monster,' Bountin said threateningly. 'But look yuh eyes on me again, and I'd fix your problems for you.'

Bountin's hand was hot and damp on the blade handle stuck in his waistband. He was ready for anything. But before he could move, Ruinsey had arm-locked his neck and was dragging him away to sit close with him, holding him there.

'Don't let them vex you, Bountey. Y'have to take it easy. Forget them. Just take it easy,' he repeated urgently.

As he spoke, the he-shes got up and sashayed downrange to the far end of the carriage.

Ruinsey had led them off the train onto a major interconnecting platform. But for the many pillars, so large it was, it could've made a full-sized concrete soccer field. They were standing now against a passage wall. Ruinsey held the directions crumpled in his hand. 'Man, I can't see how we go make it, y'know,' he said.

'How y'mean?' Bountin asked. 'She didn't write down what to do next?'

'Is not that . . . '

'Well, is what?'

Ruinsey looked away, slow eyes roving all around the big space. Shaking his head, he regarded the giant girders lying close over them. Finally, he said, 'If those things break, I wouldn't even know where I die. Not if is east, or west. Or day, or night.

And if is a crowd here when it come down, I'd die just like a common ant mashed up in a melee . . . '

'But, Ruinsey man, they have all those signs about,' Bountin said reasonably. 'Look around. Look at all those arrows, and numbers, and colours, and lines you could follow. They could – '

Ruinsey cut him off. 'Bountin, you can't see? You don't realise they only crowding you, steering people like cows, like tame animals. Y'think you could stand that? Y'could live so?'

He stopped and nodded in a final manner. Then he said, 'Yes, man, we have to take that other track.'

At Ruinsey's conclusion, a quaking notion zinged into Bountin's mind. Stubbornly, he pushed it away. Instead, he pointed up to the subway signs. 'But, Ruinsey, that is the out-town track y'looking at. We going in-town.'

Ruinsey shot him an odd look. And Bountin saw his partner's face in a new mask: one sharp and anxious, shining with greasy sweat; one with straining eyes that stared at everything too long. Then he acknowledged what was past working out. His partner really didn't want to go on anymore. For Ruinsey had turned and headed for the back-out track.

Bountin stared after him. He felt as if betrayed by some foolishness. As if his necklace charm had cut his head off, his whole spirit wilted. Vacant-minded, he stood there for minutes, until, in the distance, he heard the first urgent rushing, which before had roared into a train. That giving him life again, he sprinted off after Ruinsey.

Bountin found him before the angry dragon crescendoed past. On an inner track, it was skating farther into town. There was plenty of time for Ruinsey's train.

Their eyes made four, and all was said. They reached for and embraced each other. They were close as blood to skin, Bountin thought, and now they must bleed apart. Then they stepped back and, shy with each other for the moment, gazed together up the dark train tracks.

'I'll 'company you back to the gate, okay?' Bountin said. 'I mean, if that's all right with you?'

Ruinsey worked his vanishing-eyes smile. He said, 'Well, you settle your mind already, right, Boldman? So how could I ever stop you? Sure, make it back halfway with me.'

He handed Bountin the crumpled directions.

Another Golden Opportunity

Bapsi Sidhwe

Putli and Jerbanoo had almost identical fantasies about the land of their rulers. Their thrill was imaginative. They envisaged an orderly kingdom under the munificent authority of a British monarch based on their knowledge of the gigantic statue of Queen Victoria, cast in gun-metal and protected by a canopy of marble, in the centre of the garden in Charing Cross in Lahore. Her gun-metal Majesty had austere features and imposing rolls of flesh. She had a crown on her head and was carrying an orb and a sceptre. Her steel-trimmed mantle flowed voluminously about the throne.

Then there was the marble sculpting of the Consort astride his towering horse: bearded, haughty-eyed, a sheathed sword resting aslant his high-fitted boots.

To them England was a land of crowns and thrones; of tall, splendidly attired, cool-eyed noblemen and imposing, fair-haired ladies gliding past in gleaming carriages; of elegant lords in tall hats and tails, strolling with languid ladies who swept spotless waterfront promenades with trailing gowns, their gestures gracious and charming, marked by an exquisite reserve.

Had someone suggested to them that Englishmen, too, defecate, they might have said, 'Of course . . . they have to, I suppose,' and their exalted opinions would have been touched by doubt. But since such suggestions were not ventured, the England of their imaginings was burnished to an antiseptic gloss that had no relation to menial human toil.

When they boarded the ship at Bombay in November, their pulses throbbed enchantedly – I am going to England! I am going to England!

As the ship neared their destination Jerbanoo's heart expanded with mounting elation. She strutted about the deck, thrusting out her seal-like overcoated chest, and Faredoon found her supercilious expression painful to behold.

The effect of their imminent arrival on Putli was exactly the reverse. She shrank into herself, alarmed at the prospect of associating with a race so awe-inspiring and splendid. Her mouth pressed into a thin anxious line, her face compressed into a sharp triangle, and her eyes became more staring and humourless than ever. She snapped nervously at Freddy at the slightest pretext.

They had had their first disturbing confrontation with reality on the ship when they beheld Englishmen scour the decks and wait upon them. Within two days of landing in London their disillusionment was complete.

They saw grubby Englishmen, in ill-fitted woollen garments, scurry past with faces that betokened a concern with the ordinary aspects of life. They saw meek, unassuming men with mournful, retiring eyes; and men with the sly, cheeky eyes of street urchins. They saw seedy-looking Englishmen sweep roads, clean windows and cart garbage. They met sales girls, clerks and businessmen; all English, all white-skinned and light-eyed, on a footing of disconcerting equality. And the expression on the faces of Londoners was no different from that stamped on the faces of a cross-section of India. Where were the kings and queens, the lords and ladies and their gleaming carriages? Where were the men and women with haughty, compelling eyes and arrogant mien? They realised in a flash that the superiority the British displayed in India was assumed, acquired from the exotic setting, like their tan.

Above all, they saw Mr Charles P. Allen, on whose household they descended, scrub out his toilet bowl with a little, long-handled brush. This was the final blow! This, and the fact that Mrs Allen had no servants except for an insolent and slovenly maid who came for an hour each morning.

Mr Allen had invited the Junglewallas to stay with them. Mrs Allen, having lived long enough in India for a glimpse of its domestic intricacies, was justifiably apprehensive. Their children, Barbara and Peter, were married and living separately in London.

Mrs Allen had changed greatly since they last remembered her in Lahore. Her stylish languor and patronising air as a Commissioner's wife were replaced by the bustling abstraction of an overworked housewife. Her blue eyes were diffident, her face beginning to show a pallid large-nosed gauntness. She had permed her hair into a dull-red fuzz.

Mr Allen's corpulence was less abundant, and the beguiling flash of pink thigh tragically sealed up in flannel knickerbockers.

They lived in a square grey stone house in a row of similar houses in Finsbury Park. The house had the complicated and ingeniously contrived levels that can only be found in England. The three or four top levels and the attic were let to students. Mr and Mrs Allen occupied the ground floor and the Junglewallas were given two rooms on the half-landing to the first floor.

The hosts were overwhelmingly hospitable. Their guests charmed and overwhelmed – except Jerbanoo.

She could not reconcile herself to what she considered Mrs Allen's treacherous degradation. She remembered her surrounded by lackeys trained to jump to her bidding. She recalled her parties on flower-banked lawns. And just as she could not relate the superior Mrs Allen to the inconsequential drudge doing all the dirty housework, so she could not reconcile her fantasies of England to the commonplace Londoners. She felt greatly betrayed. Her idols toppled, as it were with a thunderous crash, leaving nothing but a pulverised residue of contempt! Scorn that turned up her nose in the air and her mouth down at the corners!

She maintained this disdainful expression throughout her stay in London.

Poor Mrs Allen, closeted with Jerbanoo while the household frolicked about London, received the full blast of her scorn. Soon Jerbanoo felt it demeaning to address such an inconsequential person as 'Mrs Allen', and took to calling her hostess 'May-ree'. Mr Allen became 'Charlie'.

Mr Allen, Faredoon and Putli went to lectures, to the theatre and sight-seeing and shopping from dawn to dusk. Jerbanoo, unable to stand the pace, went with them occasionally in the evening. She spent her time at the house tormenting Mrs Allen, meddling with her chores and generally making herself obnoxious.

Every morning she descended from the half-landing with cautious leaden thumps that boomed up to the attic, and Mrs Allen's heart sank. Jerbanoo would waddle into the kitchen and thrust an armful of clothes at Mrs Allen. 'Here, May-ree. You wash little little?'

Then she would step back into the dining room, drag a chair a few belaboured inches to the tiny fire-grate and shout, 'May-ree! Stool!'

Having appropriated the best chair in the room, and the entire warmth of the grate for the day, Jerbanoo raised her legs to the stool. Muffled in woolly scarves and cardigans, she proceeded to issue orders.

'May-ree, tea!' After the breakfast tray was lapped up, 'Finish! Take away!'

And if a rare sun was out, 'May-ree, sun, sun! I out.' Mary, trailed by Jerbanoo, would carry the chair out, pop in and fetch the stool.

If nothing else, Jerbanoo certainly exercised her smattering of English monosyllables, and by the time she left England she was able to construct adequate small sentences.

Mary, obliged to be dutiful at her husband's insistence, accommodated the old lady. She was a naturally easygoing person, worn placid by her stay in India. There she had also absorbed a compelling sense of Indian hospitality that is both profuse and slavish. She was willing to indulge her guests.

But Jerbanoo did not content herself with merely making demands. She meddled. 'Why you not make curry today?' 'Why you not cut onion proper?' 'Why you not rinse OK? I not drink with soap!' 'No chilli? I no digest!'

Sometimes her remarks were India-personal, India-insulting: 'Why you not wear nice long gown? Silly frock. It shows you got a terrible leg.' 'Why you not have bath! Water bite you?' 'You sit, you drink tea-cup every two, two minutes. Mind, demon of laziness make your bottom fat.' And once, 'Why you got no breast?' she asked, reproachfully thrusting her own abundance forward and patting Mary's flat chest. 'Not good. Poor Charlie!'

Jerbanoo touched, tampered, and tinkered with everything, poking her inquisitive nose into cupboards, drawers and larder, drawing things out for inspection. Often she summoned Mary from her work to inquire, 'May-ree! May-ree! What is this?'

At the end of two months Mary's patience wore thin.

The rain had not let up for four days. It had been a particularly trying day. Mary unwisely tried to counter the offensive by adopting Jerbanoo's methods: 'Why you so fat?' she fired. 'Why you so meddlesome? Why you so lazy?' and Jerbanoo snubbed her by snapping: 'Why you poke your nose into me, Miss?'

Jerbanoo called Mrs Allen 'Miss' whenever she wished to be especially offensive.

A little later, when Mrs Allen bent forward to adjust the fire, Jerbanoo jacked up her skirt with a fork from the dining table to examine her underwear.

Mrs Allen snapped around, whipped the fork from her hand and stood red-faced and glowering. She was trembling, too enraged to utter a word.

'Shame, shame, shame! You wearing such a small knicker!' tut-tutted Jerbanoo.

That evening Mr Allen knocked anxiously on the locked door of his bedroom, a door that had never before been locked, and discovered his wife in hysterics. The next day he had a quiet little chat with Faredoon. 'It's not that we don't like your mother-in-law, old chap. It's just that she keeps Mary at her beck and call. You know, things are different here – we don't have bearers and chokra-boys. The old dear just doesn't understand. And,' he said, lowering his voice and blushing solemnly, 'I'm afraid, she gets a bit personal every now and again.'

'My dear friend, don't speak one more word. I understand. It will be fixed!' assured Faredoon.

Jerbanoo was banished to her room on the middle landing. She was allowed down only when Faredoon or Putli were in the house.

That evening when the decision was conveyed to her Jerbanoo descended for supper in a huff. She dragged her slippered feet more than usual, sniffed, moaned, snorted, and sat down making as much noise as possible.

Mrs Allen's face was red and puffed. She met nobody's eye and spoke primly, and only when absolutely necessary.

Mr Allen carved the roast. He stood to dish it out and he served Jerbanoo a generous helping of beef, gravy and potatoes.

Jerbanoo glared at the mealy potatoes as if they were cockroaches. She stabbed them with a fork and set them aside on her sideplate with a sour expression of implacable displeasure.

The atmosphere round the dining table was strained. Putli sat mute and staring. Faredoon and Mr Allen attempted to converse with a heartiness that did not ring true.

Mary and Putli got up to clear the dishes. Her stomach full, Jerbanoo sat in slightly mollified umbrage before her mess of breadcrumbs and spilled gravy.

'Why don't you help clear the table?' asked Faredoon. 'Your legs been amputated or something?'

Jerbanoo flashed him a look of pure venom. 'Why you always poke your damn nose into me, Mister! Why?' she bawled.

But Faredoon was more able to cope with her questions than poor Mrs Allen had been. He directed a rebuking, lawyer-like finger at her. 'Because you like to poke your goddam nose into everybody's business! Tell me, you don't cook, you don't wash, you don't help at all – you are a no good guest . . . Why?'

'I have a chance? No. I never have chance!'

'All right then. I give you your chance. Tomorrow you do all the cooking.'

Mary, overhearing the conversation in the kitchen, cried: 'Oh no! There's no need for her to cook, really.' She was horrified at the thought of the devastation Jerbanoo would wreak in her kitchen.

'O yes, yes!' called Faredoon. 'She will give you a holiday . . . you two visit your children.'

Mary would not have it. But Charles later persuaded her to change her mind. They would spend Saturday with their daughter, and invite both Barbara, Peter, and their families to a dinner cooked by Jerbanoo.

There were four days to Saturday.

The Reunion

Yasmin Issacs

Year by year
they left
the land
cutting
navel string
severing bond.

Mother/father
sister/brother

Some
never to return.
Children
left
to dwell

in a well
of despair
exposed
to one
and all.
Suffering
in silence

dying
day by day

waiting
in limbo
for mothers calling.

Their reunion
had no celebration
hesitant . . .
greeting
distant
and cold.

Like the day on which she came

looks
of mirrored
anticipation

filling emptiness.

The tears
the pain

that bore this child
rush to her womb.

Carried
this life
nine long months

parted
endless years.

This lost
which was the greatest?
Should they be compared?

Moments . . .
never to share.

You wondered
what would meet you.

FEAR
flood your soul

DREAD
your mind

REJECTION
your nightmare

Her pain
Your shame.

It shaded the warmth of your smile

No blame
lay at your door

only grief
for those lost years

No blame
lay at your door

only pain
for childhood void

of

mother/father
sister/brother

sucked away
in the separation of time.

Navigator

Jane Duran

Already he's American.
He lies down in his cabin.
His head touches one end
his feet the other.
A starfish with all its arms out
feels and feels a rock.
This is what patience is.

He followed the charts first
and now they follow him.
Already he's famous,
a headdress set with gold
teetering with the far-up
feathers of the universe.

He thinks of the tiny bowed
mainland windows,
light yellow as timber.
His clothes are twisted.
The wind will kill him.
Already he has a city
at the end of a river
mild as a calf.

He wakes up in the night
and touches his burning forehead.
Already his room drags at land,
the ledges of seaweed where nobody matters.

I Sweep the Sun off Rooftops

Hanan Al Shayk

Like a thirsty horse making for water, I lunged. But I wasn't thirsty. I was on fire. I threw the water over the English boy and his friend, and the fire blazed in my head and heart and between my legs.

Images kept on coming at me which, like a crazy horse, I tried to resist, defiantly tossing my head high, but each new picture flashing into my mind enraged me more and more and I shook my head frantically from side to side.

Seeing Saad laid out on the floor, dumb and silent. Saad, whose mighty voice had welled up from his entrails. Now his wife seemed to have snatched his voice to lament for him, joined by her daughters, by his aunts and sisters, all beating their faces and rubbing ash and black soot on to their cheeks.

The English pigeon devouring the remains of the couscous, without a pause, immersing its whole beak and head in the grains while I smiled at it, saying: 'You seem to like couscous from a packet. I suppose it's because you're an English pigeon. You're used to things out of packets.'

Aisha's insistent words in the grain store, as she shook her gold earrings and the bangles on her wrist, urging me to stay at home, but I could only gaze at her shoes and marvel at how exactly they matched her handbag.

Then I am standing in Aisha's house with its Moroccan furniture and Moroccan smell, hardly able to believe that I'm in London, having braved the customs official who turned my passport over and over in his hands.

The letter with my name in English on the envelope, a Moroccan stamp, and a list of requests from my family for a white bridal veil to go with my sister's wedding dress, surgical stockings for my brother and a china dish for my mother.

Offering the blond English boy – the one I was throwing water at now – half my lunch, and sitting there full of gratitude because he smiled, because he liked the taste of the piece of chicken dipped in cumin and saffron and he had smiled at me for the first time. I wanted his approval because he was English. I wanted the approval of everyone from the bus conductor to the Pakistani shopkeeper, because he owned a shop and spoke English. Being lost in the underground, tears running down my cheeks. Learning to decipher the names of the stations. Learning them by heart as if they were magic signs.

I was throwing water at the English boy and his friend and they were yelling, 'She's crazy. Jesus Christ, she's complete crazy!'

I was transformed into a raging bull, and everything turned red. He started up at my scream and I saw the dark blood on him and on me. Then he'd jumped to his feet as if he'd been bitten by a snake, shouting, 'You're a virgin! You're still a virgin! I don't understand you.'

I didn't chew my nails with regret at giving him my virginity, furious at my weakness in lying down for him, and taking this boy in my arms just because he was English, a citizen of that great nation which had once ruled half the globe: nor did I blame myself for clinging on to an idea even though it meant severing my links with my country, and travelling to London alone without any member of my family. Instead of striking my face and grieving aloud because my hymen was no longer intact, I wondered, 'Is it because he's an Englishman that he doesn't feel proud he's taken my virginity, or is he frightened that now I'll try to force him to marry me?'

I tried to tell him that I didn't blame him for deflowering me but he wasn't listening. He just went on saying in a shocked way, as if he had lost his mind. 'You're twenty-five, thirty years old? And you're still a virgin? Jesus Christ, I don't understand you. I just don't understand at all.'

He didn't go to the bathroom to wash, he stayed in the room. Out of the corner of my eye I watched him wipe himself with Kleenex tissues and drop them on the floor, indifferent to the smears of blood on them. He pulled on his trousers and went quickly over to turn up the music, moving his head from side to side in time to the beat. He lay face down beside me, not knowing that I was now painfully aware that the threads which bound me to home and the inevitable marriage had snapped once and for all. I could see myself on the roof of our house, as, for the last time, I spread the couscous out to dry on a sheet in the sun before my journey to London: I could see the village below me: the tops of the trees, the minaret, the ancient wall which ran round my village. I could think of nothing except going to London and finding my way among its tall buildings studded with lights.

I remembered the friend of Aisha's who'd helped me escape from her house in London, carrying one of Aisha's children, while I took my suitcase and dragged the other child along with me. I could see her English neighbour shutting her front door in our faces, and yet all the same we left the two children there, rushing away after I'd pinched their cheeks to make them cry so that she'd have to come out to them.

I walked in the cold of London without tights, without an overcoat, without a jumper. In Marks and Spencer's there were hundreds of dresses and jumpers and beautiful nightdresses. I paid the woman at the cash desk and smiled at her. She smiled back and said the coat I'd chosen was really pretty. I was overjoyed. She approved of my taste and I'd given her the right amount of money for the red coat which I still haven't worn.

Eagerly I was bending over the vacuum cleaner. It was a magic broom to transport me to another world, from poverty to riches. The implements available here for cleaning were as many and as varied in colour and smell as the places which I had to clean. Aisha's gold chain which I'd carried away from her house hidden among my clothes was in my hands one moment and the next on the counter in the Oxford Street goldsmith's.

The red of my anger bubbled up like the rosy orange juice squeezed by the vendors' machines in the main street in our village. It ran down between my eyes and made me see everything blood-red, even though seconds before my mind had conjured up a pleasing vision: the English boy's sister. She was polite, she gave me a small box of chocolates with a thank-you card and kissed me and shook my hand when she came for a meal on Sunday. She had been different from her brother and from his friends who used to visit, make themselves at home in my clean room, on the clean bed, delighted to find a video and a cassette recorder and cassettes, who ate my nice food and listened to loud music and swallowed the drink they brought with them. They all said they wanted to visit my country and I nodded my head, promising it wouldn't cost them a penny, thinking how the people in the village would crowd around them, look at their coloured hair, some of it short and some long. I smiled at them, heaped more food on to their plates, poured more mint tea or coffee into their cups. I wanted their approval, even if they did smell so terrible, the reek of their hair in its stiff, bright tufts mixing with the fumes of alcohol.

I began to alter my standards of hospitality, offering them my pale, cold face when their music grew louder, when they began laughing among themselves and didn't take the trouble to explain their jokes to me as they had before, or repeat their words until I understood what they were saying. The English boy showed the others all the implements and products I had collected for cleaning and disinfecting, telling them I had a mania for cleanliness, and I'd once decided to wash all his clothes and he'd had to stay indoors the whole day.

I felt revolted by them and began to sleep in the hall, dragging a pillow and a wool blanket off the bed and leaving the room to them, in the hope that they would understand my anger, that they would no longer stay till the early hours of the morning, stepping over me as I lay asleep, leaving overflowing ashtrays and empty glasses and cans and bottles strewn about the floor. Sometimes they were so drunk they fell asleep where they were and lay without pillows or covers until I returned from work, and then I would rage at them in Arabic, telling them that thanks to them my room was no better than the Italian's pigsty at home; we used to spit on the ground whenever we went near it, children and grownups alike, shouting exclamations of disgust, even though all we could see of it was the outer fence. Why was I doing this? Pouring water over them while they yelled back at me? Perhaps this is what happened in the neighbouring rooms, which were occupied by all different people. Their noise had stopped me sleeping: shouting, shattering glass, the word 'police' echoing here and there.

How glad I'd been in those first nights with him. I'd believed the English boy would protect me from these sounds. Now they were happening right inside my own room. I tried to shout like the two of them, but my cry came out strangled and distorted; I just couldn't express my anger in English. So I reverted to the role of crazy horse, raging bull: wheeling, rearing, plunging, now attacking, now drawing back. Were they shouting? No, they were laughing. Actually laughing.

It was the music that had brought me in from the hall where I had been lying. A single note repeated over and over again, throbbing in my head, making my chest tighten. I had to be rid of them, I decided. I had to be rid of the English boy. I'd give him a choice: he could either stay on his own or leave. I knew he had no home, but that wasn't my problem. I had to go in there immediately. I had to pull the tape out of the machine, interrupt the music right in the middle of the song. It had been on loud all evening, and now it was the early hours of the morning. They had no sensitivity, no conscience.

I charged in like a bull. When I saw no one in the middle of the room, which had been full of music and smoke and pungent with the smell of hashish, I thought he might have forgotten to turn off the music before he went to sleep. I found myself thinking affectionately that I ought to be straightforward with him; the English liked that. Perhaps he didn't understand why I'd become so angry and distant. Suddenly I stopped and stood still, staring in amazement. A man was lying by his side. They were both naked. They were lying in each other's arms. I saw their uncircumcised members as clear as day and shuddered. That was the first time I'd seen a man's penis so clearly and my mouth and throat went dry. I went dry between my legs for several seconds, then I charged again. Shocked, they started up, but they made no attempt to cover their nakedness.

Then, as if they'd recovered from the surprise, they began to laugh, snorting and giggling in delight at the water being thrown at them, like two children playing a game.

I had to be dreaming. What I was seeing was surely the opposite of what was actually happening. In reality they should have been dumbfounded and embarrassed, wishing the floor would open up and swallow them. Or hiding themselves from me, resorting to a whole range of lies and excuses. How could the English boy go on living now that he'd been found out?

They continued to call on Jesus Christ, trying to dry themselves off, then laughing again. The English boy pointed to my face, unable to control his mirth. I must have looked like the mad ape that wandered the streets of our village with its gypsy owner.

Their laughter so infuriated me that I began to have thoughts of revenge. But how, when he had nothing that I could take by force, steal, hide, break in front of him, tear up or trample underfoot, to vent my rage and spite? All he owned were the clothes on his back and a few cassettes which I'd partly paid for anyway. I looked wildly about me a hundred times, unable to think what to do; then I threw my coat on over my nightdress, pulled woollen socks over the wool trousers I wore to protect me from the cold, and ran to the door, without listening to what his friend was trying to say to me. I went out and slammed the door behind me, turning the key in the lock as if I wanted to safeguard the proof of the crime and its only witnesses, repeating the same English phrase, over and over again, 'Just you wait and see.' Then I went on in Arabic: 'You'll be sorry. Everybody's going to know. I should have noticed. You've been with me for a whole week now and you might just as well have been a girl, or a boy without balls. What was I doing admiring you for being so well-behaved, sitting there for hours content to have your arm around me?' I even said to myself, 'He's English and yet he understands.' Still I wanted you to go all the way with me. London's very far . . . and I'll never go back home. I'll always live here now: I should have been on my guard. How was I to know? If you'd had a big fat bottom I might have guessed. But you're all scrawny. Your bum's hardly bigger than a fist. I'm crazy. I let your white flesh and your skinny body and your blond hair blot out things that would have made me shudder at home.'

I rang his sister from a public phone box. When she heard my voice, she asked drily, 'What do you want?'

'Your brother . . . ' I began.

She cut in. 'Are you getting me out of bed at this hour to talk to me about my brother?' she demanded.

'It's urgent,' I replied.

At this she changed her tone, and asked quickly, 'Is he all right?'

Why did I bother to tell her, only to have her shout at me, accuse me of being crazy to wake her up for that and tell me to keep my nose out of her brother's business, especially since it was nothing to do with me. As her parting shot she told me never to phone her at this time of the night again. But then her anger seemed to have woken her and she continued, 'I know you went to a lot of trouble over the meal, but my brother's sexual proclivities aren't any of your business, or mine either.'

'Bitch,' I screamed down the phone at her then, remembering how much they like dogs here, I shouted in English, 'Whore! Whore!' I walked along, trembling with anger and misery, not through the London of beautiful houses and clean streets that I'd dreamed of, where people wore only elegant, expensive clothes, nor between buildings that soared into the clouds, but in the darkness past trees planted at infrequent intervals and council houses with their unlit windows, all alike; I passed people asleep, protected from the cold in cardboard boxes, and rubbish in untidy heaps or neatly tied up in black plastic bags and empty milk bottles with traces of sour milk lingering in them, and I marvelled once again that the dairies were trusting enough to leave them lying about.

A voice rose from a heap of clothes on the pavement accompanied by the stench of alcohol-laden breath, a voice begging for a drink or money to buy a drink. I used to smile at the people who stopped me in the street, not knowing what they wanted at first, until I discovered that there were actually beggars in London. I gave them money, full of pride that I was richer than at least one English person, even if he was a beggar.

I walked along with something boring a hole between my legs. Now I was conscious of Aisha's words when we stood together in the storeroom and she tried to dissuade me from going to London: 'Go alone to London without an aunt or a husband or your mother and they'll say you've sold your soul. You'll be known as a bad girl even if you're as pure as the Prophet's daughter.'

'What you talking about?' I'd said to her nervously. 'I'll be staying with you!'

Aisha's annual visits home had sown the seed of travel in my spirit and this seed had grown and opened out and reached my eyes and tongue. On her last visit I'd been unable to take my eyes off her gold earrings and her bangles. I'd dragged her into the storeroom and begged her to take me to London, saying my family wouldn't allow me to go without her. It was not only her matching handbag and high-heeled shoes which fired my enthusiasm. The smell of couscous and other grain which filled the air constantly reminded me of my own situation. All I wanted to smell from now on was the fragrance of England which Aisha exuded. I urged her to listen to me and to feel what I was feeling. Then I took off my little gold earrings and felt in the folds of my dress for all the money I'd saved or stolen from my brother's pockets over the years, and placed both the money and earrings in the palm of her hand, forcing her fingers shut around them. As I gave her an exaggerated account of my clashes with different members of my family, she continued to discourage me, saying that the work in London was hard and that exile was no easy way of life. I thought she must not like the idea of my going on the plane with her, then coming home every year laden with presents. How could she compare the tasks of dusting and polishing the magnificent English furniture to the drudgery of cleaning our house, where there were only torn rags, a broom and a pail of water, and you had to go down on your knees to scrub the floor and do the endless piles of washing by hand?

The man at the British customs was much sterner than the magistrate who came from the capital to investigate crimes committed in our village. This man would forget the purpose of his visit, at least for a brief spell, and the fact that he was on official business, and drink tea and eat a good meal in the prosecutor's house, crack jokes and make amiable conversation, and sleep through the heat of the day. The British official behind his high desk asked me numerous questions which I didn't understand. When all I could reply were the two forlorn words, 'No English,' he asked me if I knew French. I nodded my head to find I had opened Ali Baba's cave merely by answering all his questions with the one French word, '*oui*'. His features relaxed and he stamped my passport. Without realising it he had let me know that using French words, however few and halting, has a bewitching effect upon everything in London, animate and inanimate alike.

I'd woken up the next morning at Aisha's place, not convinced that I was really in London: her flat was like any flat at home with the same smell, the same coloured ottomans and rugs, the same pictures on the walls, the brass tray in the middle of the room, and the loud shrieks and wails of her two children puncturing the air. However, this sensation evaporated as soon as I looked out of the window, when I realised how imprisoned I was by my ignorance, which Aisha seized upon, exploiting the fact that I didn't know how to flush the toilet, work the shower, turn on the oven or boil the electric kettle to make tea, and that I couldn't understand what her older child or her next-door neighbour said. I couldn't even answer the phone. Inventing far-fetched excuses, she left me trapped in her flat and made no attempt to help me look for work.

From the window I saw the flats opposite, their even lines making them look like children's drawings. Noisy voices floated through their windows. I let my gaze wander to the open grassy strip at the side of the block, which was almost completely empty of life, and then on to the red buses and cars hurrying along the main road. Fixing my eyes on them, I couldn't help cursing Aisha, wishing she was dead, swearing by the Prophet Muhammad that I would have my revenge because it was she who was stopping me walking those streets and riding in those red buses to find work and a flat or a room of my own. When Aisha returned from work, coming through the door weighed down with plastic carrier bags, her coat smelling of perfume mixed with cigarette smoke, I gave a shiver of anger: I wanted to carry shopping bags like that and wear a coat like hers!

Since everything seemed out of my reach I was reduced to making friends with the pigeons who were everywhere, and whose gentle murmurings I'd grown accustomed to hearing. I put the remains of our dinner on the window ledge to attract them, and when one of them alighted near me I called to it, 'Taste this couscous, steamed and mixed with oil, English pigeon, and tell me if it's nice.'

I'd been amazed that in London you could buy ready-made couscous in packets and that the English used it in their cooking. I'd imagined that they would eat food fit for kings, and look upon our food with distaste.

I left Aisha's prison in the following way: one day a woman

from the same village as Aisha and me came to pick up her sewing machine. She asked me if I was happy here and I sighed. She responded with an even deeper sigh. I found myself lying to her, although my lies seemed to me to represent the truth as soon as I was out of Aisha's house. I told her how Aisha kept a close watch on what I ate and drank and how I had to take care of the house and children to pay for my board and lodging. The woman nodded her head in agreement and remarked, 'Yes. Everybody says Aisha's become like an Englishwoman. She must have saved herself about thirty pounds a week having you there, because she used to pay her neighbour to look after the two children for her while she was out at work.'

Immediately we joined forces against Aisha, criticising her and insulting her. The visitor told me things about her which I didn't believe, but still I nodded my head as if to confirm what she had said. For my part, I told her that I was sure Aisha had a lover and we began searching for proof. We broke into the single, locked cupboard, and although we only found some new clothes and shoes with jewellery stuffed up inside the toes we assured each other that Aisha received money from her lover and liked leaving me in the house with the children because it made it easier to cheat on her husband.

Only the walls heard this delirious talk, but I was suddenly seized by a guilty fear, and became convinced that the two children were taking it in and that it was ringing in Aisha's ears at work, and I rushed to pack my suitcase before she came back. The visitor left, forgetting to take her sewing machine, and I left with her, knowing full well that I would never see Aisha again and that news of my forcing the lock on her cupboard would reach my family and the whole village well amplified, so that I'd end up accused of stealing all of Aisha's possessions.

I took the woman's advice and looked for work paid by the hour. I discovered that time was money and threw myself into cleaning offices, restaurants and hospitals. Picturing the pounds mounting up in my handbag, I pushed myself harder, indifferent to the veins aching with fatigue and the bits of my body which cried out with exhaustion and craved for sleep. I only stopped working frenziedly hour after hour after I met the English boy I'd just thrown water over moments before.

I left the woman's house as soon as I found work and a room to rent. When I was told I'd have to share a kitchen and bathroom with strangers I couldn't help thinking how this would astound the people at home, how they would snort with laughter at the idea that this could really happen in England, mother of civilisation. The English boy used to work in the hospital for a day at a time and then be off for several days. At tea breaks and lunchtime I never saw him eat more than a bar of chocolate or a biscuit. I never saw him talk to anybody. He would just put headphones on and close his eyes. He had blond hair, light eyes and a thin face. I suppose I fancied him although I told myself that it was just that I felt sorry for him. I decided to offer him some food. When I approached and held a piece of chicken out to him he opened his eyes in surprise and at first refused to take it. I insisted and he put out his hand, asking me if I was sure. I smiled. I no longer took what the English said seriously. 'Are you sure?' they ask without fail, regardless of whether you are offering help or an invitation to lunch, giving them a cup of tea or paying their bus fare.

After eating the piece of chicken dipped in cumin and saffron which he must have liked, he asked me where I came from. I told him and it was as if I'd opened Heaven's door. His face softened, his pupils grew bigger, and his irises went deep green like olive oil. Enthusiastically he told me that he'd always wanted to visit Morocco, live there even, and that our hashish was the best of all. Was it true, he inquired anxiously, was it really cheap there? I answered him with lies, happy that he was so interested after I'd been certain that he'd never say a word to me: I told him that I grew it myself, my family grew it, and it was everywhere like green grass and empty milk bottles in London; it was really amazing hashish: wherever I threw its seeds it sprang up like flames leaping into the air.

Dreaming of the hashish and the sunshine he said, 'You

left all that sun for the sake of these grey clouds and this miserable country?'

'What can I do with the sun?' I answered. 'Sweep it off the rooftops?'

In my imagination I could feel the monotony of the days in my country, the poverty and the nothingness. I remembered the threatening looks of the men of the family, the attentive stares from the ones in the street, my mother's harsh way of talking: and I repeated it to myself. 'What can I do with the sun? Sweep it off the rooftops?'

I was happy in London, free, mistress of my self and my pocket. Here it was impossible not to be happy. At home I was thought ugly. In one week I listened to the English boy singing the praises of my dark colouring and frizzy hair, felt him kiss me on the cheek with obvious pleasure whenever I cooked a meal and when I came in from work, or when we sat watching television together, and found him waiting for me at the end of the road when I was late back for some reason.

I encouraged the English boy to move in one evening after he had taken me to a pub, and I felt this urge to have a hold on all the different sides there were to London. Even though I didn't say a word in the uproar and drank only water, I was standing there like them in the crowds and smoke, proud and glad and sure of myself.

As soon as he entered my room that night, he declared provocatively that I must be rich to have such a bed and quilt, as well as cassettes and a television and a video. He'd expected it, he added, since he noticed that I had my own plate and cup at work, and bought tea fot whoever was sitting with me. I smiled, nodding my head, not unhappy that he'd jumped to the wrong conclusions, but surprised that he didn't know the secret of paying by instalments. He flung himself down on my bed, trying it out in different positions. 'How clean it is!' he exclaimed. 'How comfortable! I've never slept in a bed like this before.'

Was I hearing him right or had I missed the point as so often happened? When we talked it was like two people playing with a ball: sometimes it went into the goal, sometimes it grazed the post, but most of the time it went high in the air and missed completely. He hadn't slept in a bed like that before, yet there were all those advertisements for them on television, and they were on display in shop windows and in almost all the big stores in London so that I'd imagined them in all the houses I could see from the bus.

Quite at home in my bed, he fell fast asleep until dawn.

In the little streets and neighbourhoods where I wandered, London did not sleep. And when it did, the hoardings stayed wide awake. Hoardings about films, pop concerts, milk, drugs and AIDS . . . AIDS? My thoughts suddenly became alert: he was going to die of AIDS. I should tell him, extending my finger in a threatening manner: 'You'll die of AIDS.' Then I found myself shouting, inside my head, *'I'll die of AIDS. O, my God!'*

Then partly reassured, I thought, 'He entered me twice, but he came outside me.' Then again I cried out in terror, wordlessly, 'Who knows? Maybe a germ slipped out of his prick and landed on me.' And with an involuntary movement I raised my eyes to the sky – where God was – beseeching Him, wanting Him to see my fear and my contrition. But I couldn't see the moon or the stars, only the gloomy sky. I lowered my head quickly, as if to acknowledge the truth spoken by the old woman Khadija when she heard of my decision to travel to London. 'Foreigners have no God,' she claimed, as if she wanted to weaken my resolve and then, correcting herself and asking God's pardon, she changed this to 'Our God, the God of Islam, is different from theirs in the West.'

Then, again asking God's forgiveness, she said that there was no God, but God, and the trouble was that Westerners didn't follow His instructions or live by His law. At this she rose, washed her mouth ten times to make amends and performed twenty prostrations for her scepticism.

I had to go back to the room, as if I needed to tell the place where I lived of my feeling. As I accelerated my pace I asked myself what I was doing here, and I didn't know the answer. Why didn't I go home to my own country taking with me the sheet which bore the stains of my virginity? I had purposely left it unwashed, stuffing it in a suitcase because I might need to spread it out on my bridegroom's bed in the dark of night. Bridegroom? I would save some money and then I would find a man to marry me, especially if I promised to bring him to London. But why was I here? Was it because I was out of reach of the prying eyes of the men in my family and their questions about my comings and goings, and far from my mother's interrogations about why I slept on my stomach, or why I took so long in the bathroom? The God of my far-off country must remember that I used to pray four times a day and still love me. Now I had to be on my guard against AIDS and the Devil. I opened the front door and heard the voice of Warda Al-Jazairiyya flooding through the door of my room. Pushing the door open, I was confronted by a tall, blond, green-eyed version of myself, the Englishman's friend dressed up in my clothes, with my kohl on his eyes, wearing a pair of my earrings. He was swaying his head in time to the Arab song.

I stood before my blond other self, wondering at my calmness, contemplating my clothes on the English boy's friend. After the long conversation with my brown self out in the street and being confronted now by a blond self, the haze lifted and all the images became clear.

I no longer had to push away the picture of Saad laid out on the floor, or banish from my imagination the sound of his huge voice, louder than the roaring of the wind, dumb for ever. The women of the family struck their faces and smeared them with soot. Saad had taken his own life the night the news had gone round that he'd been caught sleeping with a travelling shepherd. He could speak no longer: he'd swallowed his voice, choking on the words, while his wife's voice, which had always been weak and incoherent before, rose high into the air, followed by those of his daughters and his sisters. When Saad's note proclaiming his innocence was discovered there was an outcry in the village. Saad's family rushed to try and have their revenge on the witness who had announced the news like someone possessed, and who cared less about Saad's death than about convincing the whole community of what he had seen in the hut that burning noonday. The village was divided between those who wanted Saad's name cleared and those who wanted the accusation against him proven even after his death. His soul would have no response and would hover over the place, flying through the night.

As I remembered I laughed. My blond self laughed at the people of my village. I imagined Saad lying down with the English boy and the two of them flirting and giggling together. The boy came over and put his arm round me, as if he could not quite believe my laughter and my lack of agitation. I smiled at both of them and told his friend my clothes suited him. He asked if I had a caftan he could borrow. I shook my head regretfully – I hadn't brought it with me, thinking the English would look down on my caftan with its silver belt – although I saw garments like it selling here at huge prices. I was still laughing. I imagined the beggar from the London streets sitting with the old woman Khadija in my village. I had a mental picture of the conductor on the red London bus talking to Hammouda the village postman, of the English boy's friends playing with Khadija's grandson, especially Margaret, whose hair reminded me of the coloured feather duster Khadija's grandson had pleaded for every time he saw it in the market, thinking that it was a toy or a bird. I saw Margaret talking to Saniyya, the daughter of the woman who ran the bath-house. I saw people springing up from the ground and letting down ropes out of the sky, boarding red buses, jabbering in English. Englishmen climbing the ancient village wall with their bowler hats and black umbrellas. Englishwomen, some pushing their pushchairs along the winding muddy roads, other older ones fanning their faces with trembling hands and still wearing their coloured woolly hats.

The television blared, and then I noticed the electricity

advertisements: an electric stove, an electric heater, an electric boiler. I'd have to buy an electric boiler to replace the gas one which had been leaking for a week now. The gas man had told us it would blow up and had stuck on a warning sign to remind us.

I turned, intending to ask the English boy why he lived with me, why he liked my company. Once he had said I showed him a concern which he had never met with before, even from his parents, and that he would love to visit my country one day. At the time I didn't believe him because I wasn't used to hearing the truth from people's lips, preferring to believe what I thought rather than what I heard.

Instead I found myself thinking 'AIDS'. I looked at the two of them. 'You ought to go and have yourselves examined.'

I was thinking I would boil the sheets that evening and ask the chemist for a powerful disinfectant and give myself a vinegar douche to get rid of all the germs inside me.

They went into the kitchen and I started to tidy the room, gathering the plates from here and there and scattering the remains of the food on the window ledge. The pigeons flocked around it immediately, though dawn was only just breaking. I knew the neighbours complained that the pigeons grew used to coming close to the windows, but I didn't care. 'Eat up,' I told the nearest bird. 'You're lucky I'm feeding you, not eating you. Where I come from, if we see a pigeon we throw a stone at it. If it falls we accept our good fortune, kill it and eat it. If it carries on flying we shrug our shoulders and say, "It's the angels' turn today." You're not beautiful, you're not white, or even a nice light brown. You're grey and black like a big rat, but I love you because you're English and you wait for me every day.'

Yeast

Briar Wood

The nomadic group Julie and Paul had belonged to was dispersing across the high rise, suburbs and hostels of London. Now they were all the more lost to each other than they had ever been on the backpacking trail. The novelty had gone from conversations with slackers in youth hostels, local people prepared to talk to outsiders, earnest soul seekers searching for themselves. When asked if New Zealand still had that Prime Minister people went overseas to escape, Paul shrugged and Julie said she didn't even know who was Prime Minister any longer. They stayed silent in what seemed like endless discussions of immigration policy, Britain's membership of the EEC, the state of the job market, the cancelled Springbok tour and nuclear-free seas. The working holiday was turning into a full-time job hunt.

Paul had been looking for work as a sports journalist. With seven years of everything from schoolgirl netball to international rugby tournaments behind him he'd thought it would be a breeze. Well-wishers slapped him on the back when he left New Zealand and said he was sure to land on his feet; they loved Kiwis over there because they were such hard workers. This turned out to be accurate enough when it came to jobs like au pairing and furniture removal, but you had to be quick, lucky and obsequious to get in the door to anything else. Now they were on the bread line and the only thing he had to show for all those interviews was a range of unspoken replies to sheep jokes.

On top of the employment hassles, they weren't getting on. They'd become casual lovers after an introduction years earlier by relentlessly sociable friends and then perversely got together more seriously a few weeks before Paul was due to leave for Sydney with Mark, his closest friend. Julie was doing costumes for a community theatre and when it packed up, she joined them in Sydney. It took some determination to detach Paul, as the two men had embarked on a long-haul tour of the city's pubs, but Julie worked on his wanderlust and their last sighting of Mark sipping a solitary pint in the airport bar had even wrung a small splash of sympathy from her.

A letter containing news that Mark was in Britain found them at a camping ground on Mykonos, two years later. By the time they reached London, Mark, whose degree was in marketing, was established as an accountant for a small construction firm in Brighton, subcontracted to a bigger firm building a supermarket. He'd bought a flat, and said they could polish his floor any time, adding that there was bound to be work of some kind for Paul to do.

It might, Paul and Julie agreed, be better than trying to hustle in London. They expected people to be friendlier and the air cleaner in Brighton, though the sum total of their knowledge of the seaside town added up to images of the Mods and Rockers having rumbles on the rocky beach and Julie's Aunt Sally, the only British relative she knew of, dying of pneumonia in a bedsit. Sally's second husband, who she ran off with after the first one went to jail for a dodgy business deal, was a movie producer, and when they parted, Sally came from LA to live with Julie's grandparents. Life on the farm was too flat for her and she went back to Brighton, where she had grown up, to die.

Julie moved into Sally's room after her brother was born. The carpet design was blue roses and there were thick white curtains. While she was small it smelt of roses, powder and chocolates. Last time she'd slept there, just before she'd left for Sydney, she could smell only the dampness of the bush, separated from the house by a thin strip of grass. She'd stayed awake a long time, listening to the *needdeep needdeep* of frogs in the water tank.

The site manager arranged for Paul to start straight away, especially after Mark let it slip that his friend had played counties cricket. Despite typing skills of the single-fingered variety, Julie got offered a job as a secretary in a massage parlour, but changed her mind when Mark asked if he and Paul could get in for free. Finally the Anne of Cleves took her on as a barmaid. The flat she chose was small and cold and it cost too much, but there was a tiny round window in the bedroom, a ship's porthole, through which they could see a thin line where the dark grey of sea ended and the light grey of sky began. It'll be like living in a bubble,' she said, describing the flat to Paul. They had to borrow money off Mark for the bond because Paul spent their savings on a rust bucket with a good motor to get himself to work and back. Then Mark's girlfriend Kelly, who had been travelling in Scandinavia, returned with a man in tow. She said it was a platonic astral-type relationship. Whatever friendship it was, three was a crowd in the living room. 'Sorry mate,' Paul told him. 'You'll have to sort Kelly out yourself.'

Tension brewed into an argument as they moved their possessions. Paul thought the flat was a waste of dough and told her so. Mark's was a lot cheaper. Or they could check out the possibility of living in at the pub.

'We have to get ahead,' he insisted.

'Ahead of what?'

'Go up in the world. I don't want to drive a heap like this for the rest of my life.'

'Oh yeah, like when we were in Nepal and you never wanted to own anything. Now Mark's got a flat and you want one too. I don't want to stay here any longer than it takes to get a fare together.'

'Why don't we stay at Mark's, then? It's all right for people like you with haciendas to go back to.'

'I can't go back,' she protested.

He drove as fast as he could past tightly packed hillsides of houses in Moulsecoomb. Not many of the flats on those frost-crunched hillsides had gardens, or even a tree in the backyard. A few mangy shrubs and that was it. The homes looked much smaller than the rented farmhouse near a railway where he'd grown up. Trains sliced the nights of his childhood to ribbons. Arguments over dinner, sometimes humorous, other times bitter. His three sisters now lived in various small towns across the world.

Summer dropped off the trees. They walked out to look at the piers. One was full of space invader machines and the other, bought by American developers, was inaccessible after a failed attempt to dynamite it. Neither said so, but something was missing; that ingredient, whatever it was, that had kept everything unsettled, made them light-headed in each other's company. Travelling had become so much a way of life that they found it hard to imagine or enjoy the idea of an existence in which they might know the name of their doctor, play chess or look up a recipe.

Paul had to be on the job by eight, six days a week. He'd drive, shrugging off tiredness, his hands numb through the acrylic gloves on the steering wheel, to pick up a pallid, wasted Krysztof. Often they shared a joint on the way to work. Krysztof had been an actor in Poland but hadn't even seen a stage in the ten months since he'd come to Britain. He lived in a bedsit without running water and wore the same clothes all week, except Sunday, when he washed them.

On site they were digging and concreting foundations. The sun still showed up on a good day, but there was always a jagged sea wind. A lucky man was the one who got a job in the most sheltered position on the site. During November the cold and damp intensified and escape was impossible, no matter how many layers of clothing they wore, or where they went among the scaffolding and machinery. For the first hour they had to take care not to rip any muscles. Then they warmed up a bit and it was only another hour before tea break. Most Fridays, Paul met Mark at the pub and they exchanged news about home.

Across the road from the flat was a trendy bakery called Pain which kept magazines and coffee and sold a mixture of breads and pastries. Sometimes in the morning the two rooms in the flat warmed and seemed to swell with the aroma of freshly baking bread. On those days they couldn't resist stopping. Over breakfast, they got talking to Luisa and Ignacio who lived next door. The women called round on each other to discuss everything from Argentina to families and telepathy. Julie arranged a Friday evening off work to cook for the four of them.

Paul figured he had time for a few rounds. He put some money in the jukebox, as he always did. It cheered him to know that 'I See Red' was being played in a pub in the south of England. The boys were talking about Michael Delaney, who'd been laid off the day before, supposedly because he wasn't needed any more. Krysztof said there must be something behind it because the foreman told him his nephew was starting in a week's time. According to Sean, Krysztof could've misheard, since his English wasn't up to much. Someone asked if the fact that Michael went around handing out Socialist Workers' Party pamphlets and trying to get people to go on holiday camps had anything to do with it. Paul forgot about the dinner and then someone asked him why Julie wasn't at work so he skulled his drink and left. Back at the flat, everything was ready. He only had to change. But Julie seethed and at the dinner everyone was fractious.

Saturday he woke late with a hangover, to the usual sound of morning TV. His foot throbbed where it had been crushed against a wall, unloading bricks. On screen, a reporter was interviewing Kent miners who were busing to London to join a march. Paul asked if there was any milk but Julie didn't answer. She just kept staring at the television. He started telling her about Michael Delaney and how it was terrible that anyone at work who tried to join a union or even looked like they might, got sacked on some pretext or another. She commented that back home he hadn't had much time for unions.

'I thought you came from the send-them-back-where-they-came-from-if-they-don't-know-they're-lucky-to-have-a-job school of personnel management.'

'Shut up,' he told her. 'You've never worked on a building site so what do you know about it?'

The row was so loud that Ignacio and Luisa banged on the wall. It was one of those action replay ones where they both recounted an oral history of everything the partner or anyone in the partner's family had ever done to offend them. When they stopped for breath, Paul suggested that he drive them both out to Beachy Head where they could use up more energy walking and shouting at the same time. Julie was wearing a thin denim jacket and the cold paid it no attention. She said she wanted to drive to the pub at Devil's Dyke to meet Luisa, but he said no, he was driving. He put his foot down. Hard.

'Drive slower!' she called urgently as they overtook a truck on a sharp, icy corner climbing over the Downs. The indicator jerked higher. A car pulled out of a driveway and Paul stabbed at the brakes, shouting out the window:

'Watch where you're bloody well going!'

'You shouldn't talk to people like that. You're the one who should watch where you're going. You're speeding.' She looked to him like a bird trapped indoors, flinging herself against the glass of a closed window. He pulled up in the car park, brakes shrieking, got out and shouted: 'Don't you fucking tell me what to do!' A couple turned to stare.

Mark bought them all a drink, then asked if the ladies would mind if he and Paul went and played pool.

'What did you want to come and live here for? New Zealand looks so beautiful,' said Luisa. 'I know! It's the Pavilion, isn't it?' Julie managed a smile.

'You can't eat scenery.'

'Brighton has good food, clubs. It's a sociable place.'

'But it's not so small that it's stifling?'

'Right. I like to know a lot of people, but it's good to be able to disappear if you want to. Like, see that guy over there?' He was standing at the bar, talking with the couple from the car park – dark business suit and slicked-back hair; in his late forties, early fifties.

'He's in the antiques trade now, but he used to be a big-time crim in the East End. He came back down here quietly after a few years on the Costa del Crime.' The man was looking in their direction. Luisa smiled and raised her glass.

'How do you know?'

'I've got a friend who's a secretary in a law firm – she introduced me to him. She had a fling – a fling, is this the right word? – with him once. She told me. He calls himself Andrew but that isn't his name.' A barmaid came over with some drinks.

'Compliments of 'im.' Luisa waved him over. He talked in Spanish with Luisa, translating everything for Julie and then asked her about herself.

'I'm impressed,' she told him laughing after a discussion about the problems of staging fringe productions in West End theatres.

'Look, one of the stage managers owes me a favour – I'll give him a ring and see if there's any work going in your line.' Julie gave him her number in exchange for his card.

'He's a bit of a charmer, isn't he? He fancies you. I can tell.'

'Maybe he's just being friendly.'

'Get real, Julie. From what I've heard he's the kind who expects value for money.'

'Doesn't everyone? Maybe what you've heard is just hearsay.'

'You'd never know he was a killer, would you?'

'He murdered someone?'

'More than one.'

On the way home, Luisa stopped the car. The colour had leached from her face. She thought probably it was only the beer, but asked Julie to drive.

A note slipped under the door next morning said: 'Dear Julie. We had to go to the doctor last night and she informed us that my wife is pregnant. Luisa asked me to tell you she will stay with friends in London.'

It was mostly quiet at the pub. Andrew came in for lunch sometimes. Once he brought her some tickets for *The City of Mahogany*. Julie took her second cousin, who had just arrived in London and was working in a shoe shop in Oxford Street, to a matinée production. On the way back from London she got off the train at a small station called Wivelsfield because she liked the name of it and wanted to watch the snow sifting down.

A young woman in a solid coat came in out of the snow, sat down and pulled out a book. Julie asked her when the next train was and she said in forty minutes because she'd meant to catch the 4.15 but had had one last drink and just missed it.

'Do you live around here? It's just how I imagined English countryside would be.'

'What do you mean?'

'Stone walls, hedges, oak trees.'

'I hate it!' said the woman. 'It's Celia and Henry territory. Revolting.'

'Who?'

'You know. Boring middle-class couples. Neighbourhood Watch. Double glazing. Speaking of which, I've just been to visit my parents. I needed some money to pay a fine for cutting through the wires at Greenham. Had to sit through a lecture to get it, but they came around.'

'Are you living at Greenham?'

'No. I just went down for the day. I didn't mean to get arrested – I didn't even know we were actually going to dismantle the fence until these women I was with got the tools out of their bags. Didn't tell my parents that though. Are you Australian?'

'No, I'm from New Zealand.'

'Oh. I'm really sorry.'

'Why? Because I am a New Zealander or because you thought I was an Australian?'

'Or for myself because I can't tell the difference?'

By the time the train pulled in under the elaborate ironwork of Brighton station, Julie knew so much about the lives of all the people in Kate's flat that she felt like a personal column. They traded addresses. Kate suddenly hugged her and said she hoped they'd get together again soon.

'Come around any time. I'll call you next time I'm going to Greenham. I got offered a lift with some smelly hippies but I'm going to sort something else out.' Julie walked back to the flat trying to imagine how she would pay a fine if she got imprisoned for breaking into a top-secret military base.

A few days later, on a Friday, a ditch collapsed at the supermarket site and Sean and Krysztof nearly got buried. Paul lost it and shouted at the foreman about how he was going to join a union to make sure this sort of thing didn't happen again. He woke on Saturday with an aching back and knew he wasn't going anywhere, even though they sometimes got a day's wages just for working the morning. Julie called to him that maybe they could go out for lunch. He'd already told her that he wanted to write some letters and phone his aunt in Liverpool so he pretended to be asleep while she dressed. She sat on the edge of the bed beside him.

'You're not wearing that purple skirt, are you?'

'What's wrong with it?'

'It's a bit – Maori.' She got up, picked up her bag and coat deliberately, slamming the door with enough force to shake the windows. There had been a fresh snowfall overnight but the day was riding high and bright.

Luisa was sitting on the wet doorstep, her head in her arms, sobbing loudly.

'Where have you been?' Julie put an arm around her. 'What's wrong?'

'Ignacio. He doesn't understand this cooking makes me sick and he is still expecting me to do it.'

'Do you want to come for a walk?'

Ignacio slid through the door and stood awkwardly watching them.

'I'll talk to you later,' Luisa said, then went inside with him.

At Marine Parade Julie was shown straight to Kate's bedroom. Kate was in bed with someone who introduced himself as Alan. Backing out, Julie said she'd come back later but Kate said no, just give her a few minutes to get dressed. A bunch of people was watching rescue teams on television drag a body from the rubble of a multi-storey building with several floors blown away. The camera moved over a face stiff in pain. Some of the viewers in the living room laughed and cheered.

'Oh just hurry up and die,' Kate said, as the man on the screen was carried off on a stretcher.

'It was that close! What a celebration we could'a had.' Ben opened a can.

'Imagine – no more marches shouting "Maggie Maggie Maggie, Out, Out, Out." You'll have to think of something else to chant,' Martin, his lover, got in quickly.

The scene on the television shifted to show the face of the President of the US. There was a hunt for the remote control but nobody could find it. Ben pulled the plug at the wall.

'Hey – did ye hear the story about the old miner billeted with Sarah's parents? They gave him muesli for breakfast and he asked what it was.'

'We're going walking in Preston Park,' Kate announced into a kitchen crowded with people making popcorn and arguing about the *Belgrano*.

Crocuses poked through the snow by the trees, blue as a gas flame. Curled in a sunspot in the Willow Pattern garden was Andrew. He sprang up to tell them they were just in time to come with him to an auction where a defunct theatre company was selling off costumes.

Clothes, hats, shoes and props spilled out of the crates. He held an elaborately beaded flapper's dress against Julie.

'What do you think?'

'More my style. What about this for Jules?' Kate picked out a Jackie Onassis style minidress.

Julie rejected both suggestions and went over to watch the auction. She bid for a double bed.

'Who is this guy?' Kate asked in the toilets.

'A friend of a friend.'

'He's a right Flash Harry. Should be good for a few drinks at least.' She mouthed 'Show me the way to the next whiskey bar' and pouted into the mirror. But Andrew had to get back to one of the shops and he dropped Kate at the flat. Then he asked Julie if she had time for a quick drink. Paul and Mark arrived at the Anne of Cleves while Andrew was buying their third round. He waited until they began talking to the publican before returning to Julie, saying he didn't realise it was so late and he'd better go.

'Don't open this until you get home.' He pushed a plastic shopping bag with some soft fabric item inside it into her hands.

She hid the flapper's dress in the bag under the washing. As Paul was putting out the light, she remembered to tell him about the bed she'd bought.

'No map of Australia?'

'No map.'

'I might be going to Manchester. There could be a job.'

'I could come. I'd like to try Manchester.'

'We're staying with Mark's sister.'

'We?'

'Yeah. Mark and me. There's no room for you as well.'

She covered her head with a pillow. For a few seconds sleep swirled and she was losing consciousness when her mouth filled with the yeasty taste of beer. It was fresh and sharp, as beer tasted in a garden bar on a hot Hamilton summer evening, like those days when she and Paul would play tennis after work.

'What are you thinking of?' she asked drowsily.

'The different brews I was trying tonight. Why?' She sat up.

'I just had the strongest taste of beer in my mouth.'

'Really?'

She turned over and closed her eyes, but stayed tensely awake, as if her mind was a room Paul had stepped into when she didn't expect him and wanted to be alone.

'What were you talking to that man about?'

'What man?'

'Mr Smooth.'

'Must've been a customer.'

'Who is he? Suit and gold chain. Seems pretty familiar with you.'

'Oh – Andrew. He's a businessman. Comes into the pub a lot. Used to be a big-time crim.'

'Looked like a regular guy to me.'

'I've never talked to a murderer before. Luisa says he's famous. Used to date models and go to celebrity parties in the sixties. So, when are you going to Manchester?'

'Next week.'

'I might run off with a gangster while you're there.'

'What – with that sleazeball? Be my guest.' A silence settled between them until he broke it.

'Anyway, I think I killed someone once.'

'You what?'

'A hitchhiker. On my way home from New Plymouth. When I was selling sports clothes. It was the week after one of the guys in the flat did a runner with our stash of grass. Owed three months' rent as well.'

'Since when did you pick up hitchhikers?'

'Dunno why I stopped. I'd been on the road a few days – maybe I wanted the company. He looked waterproof, but harmless. Except he was a nasty little brute. Started being rude to me right away – sneering at my music, haircut, my sports jacket.'

'Maybe you took it the wrong way.'

'No, he was full of aggro. He wanted to wind me up.'

'Doesn't sound like it took much.'

'He'd been visiting some place called Jerusalem. Was on his way back to a commune up north. Said people like me are just propping up the system. So I stopped the car and told him he was a waster and there is only one system. What did he think living in a system meant?'

'You didn't leave him there?'

'That's what he said. Started whingeing. You can't leave me here, he said. Like hell I can't, I told him – he should've thought of that before he got on my nerves.'

'What time was it?'

'Sunset. He cursed at me and wouldn't move. So I got out of the car and went round to his side and dragged him out. He was trying to lock the door but I got hold of him and we were punching the shit out of each other. I head-butted him a few times and then I just kept smashing him. His head felt like jelly after a while. Eyes rolled right back and his head flopped around. I pushed him in the bushes and took off.'

'You don't know if he died.'

'He didn't look healthy.'

'Didn't you go back?'

'Yeah. He wasn't there.'

'Maybe he woke up and crawled away.'

'Doubt it. He was sick as.'

'You sure have got a temper.' Julie rolled into a foetal position.

'Only when provoked.'

She was asleep when he offered a penny for her thoughts.

The Machine That Cried

Michael Hofmann

'Il n'y pas de détail' – *Paul Valéry*

When I learned that my parents were returning
to Germany, and that I was to be jettisoned,
I gave a sudden lurch into infancy and Englishness.
Carpets again loomed large in my world: I sought out
their fabric and warmth, where there was nowhere
  to fall . . .

I took up jigsaw puzzles, read mystical cricket thrillers
passing all understanding, even collected toy soldiers
and killed them with matchsticks fired from the World
  War One
field-guns I bought from Peter Oborn down the road
– he must have had something German, with that
  name –

who lived alone with his mother, like a man . . .
My classmates were equipped with sexual insults
for the foaming lace of the English women playing
Wimbledon,
but I watched them blandly on our rented set
behind drawn curtains, without ever getting the point.

My building-projects were as ambitious as the
  Tower of Babel.
Something automotive of my construction limped across
  the floor
to no purpose, only lugging its heavy battery.
Was there perhaps some future for Christiaan Barnard,
or the electric car, a milk-float groaning like a sacred heart?

I imagined Moog as von Moog, a mad German scientist.
His synthesiser was supposed to be the last word in
  versatility,
but when I first heard it on Chicory Tip's
Son of my Father, it was just a unisono metallic drone,
five notes, as inhibited and pleonastic as the title.

My father bought a gramophone, a black box,
and played late Beethoven on it, which my mother was
  always
to associate with her miscarriage of that year.
I was forever carrying it up to my room,
and quietly playing through my infant collection of singles,

Led Zeppelin, The Tremeloes, *My Sweet Lord* . . .
The drums cut like a scalpel across the other instruments.
Sometimes the turntable rotated slowly, then everything
went flat, and I thought how with a little more care
it could have been all right. There again, so many things

were undependable . . . My first-ever British accent wavered
between Pakistani and Welsh. I called *Bruce's* record shop
just for someone to talk to. He said, 'Certainly, Madam.'
Weeks later, it was 'Yes sir, you can bring your children.'
It seemed I had engineered my own birth in the new
  country.

Prayer

Mimi Khalvati

has nothing of the grandeur
or the violence of crowds
but circles, stockinged,
in its own quiet sphere

like lamplight sealing off what gloom sees
by its cone against the dark,
an interval when, weightless,

the body loses cut and thrust,
rises like a plume of smoke
to add its grievances to air's.

Prayer
is like watering the plants,
popping out to get the paper,
a trundling, pottering,

an audience for dust
that settles even as the duster's hand
moves across the grain.

Prayer can interrupt itself – fling
instructions over a shoulder, offer
delicacies on a shelf;

resume itself, its murmuring,
like berries, herbs
left drying in the sun

as, moving out of earshot,
you find your own momentum,
your freedom not to pray.

Prayer is not a scourge.
Though the head bows, back stoops,
it is a lifting, a soft and drifting
spiral like the echoes of a string plucked,

a sky to feel alone in,
how small one is, how packed
the earth with people;

how far the neighbour's radio
– as skin meets stone – recedes
and amber beads count amber suns
that are still to rise, still to set.

Prayer is a time of day
that, on a winding stair,
greets itself.

Camels

Jane Duran

for Syra

On your first day of secondary school
we set off in a minicab.
I know you've been awake since dawn,
preparing, worrying in your room
blue and draped as a tent.
Your braids are tightly knit.
Hands in your lap.
The small red and white checks
of your collar stick out
over your grey wool coat
like the slightest mention
of candlelight in a village
before morning, that first voice.

The driver is Moroccan, lifts out
Andalus from the loudspeaker
to remind us of the shimmering world
beyond the school, its breathlessness
and turquoise particles never ceasing,
the camels with their wide-of-the-mark
and fluid sidestepping, blinking
with their great neutral eyelids

sand-light, night,
their own lives whirling within them
far from our own, on the way
to school in a minicab.

The school is still far,
floating over Regent's Park.
You take out your new pencil case
with nothing missing.
We trail the Andalus song
like a slow scarf, like a beach-tide
across the windows of the car.
We can see over the gates of the school.
The other children arrive –
they are all courageous.
You take the measure of them
when their camels drop to their knees
and they slide down the rugs,
the four corners slipping.

The older girls wait
at the top of the steps,
bend down tenderly,
ask your name.

The Mulberry Tree

Joan Riley

The July heat is increasingly oppressive as the hands on the clock creep towards midday. A pall of dust from the construction site opposite the low-rise rehabilitation unit sits heavily on the still air. The flow of cricket commentary from the workman's transistor on the outside windowledge gives way to a round-up of the midday news.

Inside, the monotonous whirr of the electric fan stirs the thick air which clings in damp patches under her arms and along her spine. The radio announcer give a brief warning about poor air quality before handing back to the day's play at Edgbaston. The news that the West Indies pace bowlers have once again demolished the English batting order makes her smile. Pride tinges the anticipation of watching her team at the Oval grounds the following week. It draws some of the ache from the home-sickness which give bittersweet edges to the warmth and colour of English summer days.

In Jamaica she hated cricket, fancied herself too sophisticated for the regular pilgrimage to Sabina Park whenever a touring side was playing; much less the weekly turn-out at the local school grounds for the National League matches.

Things are different now. Her culture in England is a mean harvest, driven into enclaves and evolved into alien shapes. Here she no longer has the riches of familiarity. Could not feel dislike, detachment or indifference for cricket, independence celebrations or the forays into establishing a Trinidad-style carnival on the streets of Kingston in recent years.

She thinks back to the wet windy September morning of her arrival four years ago, the sick sense of apprehension as the enormity of her decision dawned on her. Steve had been late collecting her; the familiar face strange and distant with a close cropped haircut, body hidden under suit and bulky overcoat. England too had wrapped him in layers. Strange habits and preoccupations with real and imagined grievances she could not understand.

He had been different on the Island, wooing her with carefree words and large ambitions. He came down every year for five years. One month at a time. They met on his first trip. Wrote long letters of discovery in the separation that followed. In the second year he was passionate about island politics and had dreams of permanent return. Year three found him planning to take a master's degree to improve his prospects. By year four she realised he would not emigrate, yet when he offered marriage she accepted. England held no attraction for her, but she wanted him and he could not part with his life there.

Now their only remaining connections are his irrational jealousy, the fear that colours thoughts of him and her hunger for Jamaica. In self-defence she clings to every small reminder of the old country. She bought a Walkman to have portable access to the latest cricket score. Keeps it hidden at work in case Steve finds it and punishes her for spending good money without his agreement.

August bank holiday finds them trekking to the other side of London. Wedging deep into the spectator crowd as Notting Hill transforms into the Caribbean for a day. The grey streets of London are far from the wide blue horizons of her homeland, but she married him. Against her family's wishes, for better or for worse. His dreams, his world had to become hers. So each year she makes her pilgrimages of sanity, to Notting Hill,

Kennington Oval, the Commonwealth Institute. Seeking skin tones in browns and black, voices from elsewhere, the illusion of sameness and belonging.

Hurried footfall in the corridor brings back the reality of the busy head injury unit. Slower, dragging, hesitant steps, the babble of voices tells her lunchtime is over and afternoon sessions about to begin. The wall clock is showing 1.20 p.m. On the radio cricket has given way to the afternoon phone-in dominated by the latest round of sleaze stories about the ruling Conservative Party.

Her grumbling stomach is a reminder that her lunch is overdue. She pushes aside the open file and reaches for her identity card on the windowsill. The name beneath the stiff formal picture catches her attention. Perlene Draycott. Even after four years it remains alien. Inside her head she is still Lena – Lena Williams as she was known until Steve changed all that. Once she joined him in England he told her he did not like the shortened version of her name.

She tried to argue, stung by his sudden about-face. She had been Lena all her life, apart from the moments she was christened and registered. The name had not bothered him in all those years of courtship so why did it bother him the moment she set foot in Britain?

He told her she was going to be living in England, that London wasn't some backwater island full of ragged, barefoot children. Angry at the unjustified attack, Lena pointed out his name was also shortened. Steve settled the argument in a way she was to learn well over the next four years. It was weeks before she was able to discard the concealing scarf and dark glasses. Isolated, alone in a strange country without family and friends, she was too ashamed to write home and too afraid to run.

Rising abruptly, she gives herself a mental shake as she pins the card to the pocket of her cotton blouse. Gathering up her purse and the sandwich bought on the journey into work, Lena heads for the door, determined not to let him invade the rest of her working day.

*

The old man stands in his customary place, the fraying edges of the tall grass giving the illusion his crumpled figure has grown and tarnished with the unkempt landscape and the misshapen tree. *Her tree.* She discovered this neglected and forgotten corner of the hospital grounds the week she started work. For two years it had been her private space until *he* suddenly appeared six weeks ago.

The grass is littered with deep purple. Over-ripe fruits falling unheeded from the ladened branches. The plop, plop, plop of their periodic fall makes small definite statements in the echoing summer silence. He shuffles back against the trunk bowed and frail, a light summer breeze teasing through the few long strands of grey clinging stubbornly to the sweating bald pate. His age-wasted body in the sagging brown suit blends to the sturdy thickness of a century and a half of growth. He is deep in some other landscape, one hand caressing the sturdy branch thrusting horizontally across the gentle slope beneath which the roots are bedded. The eyes are almost lost beneath the wrinkled folds of brown speckled skin as he squints through the sunlight at the high branches silhouetted against the pale blue and concrete grey of the urban skyline.

She stands hesitant and uncertain on the overgrown path a few feet away, tempted by the cool shadows, but not wanting to share her tree.

The old man senses her presence. He turns slowly, head lowering until grey eyes focus with unexpected sharpness. 'We had a tree like this.' The voice is a shock in the rumpled English landscape, the soft slur of somewhere in West Coast America where she expected the flattened vowels of south London.

Lena stares at him. A typical old man, indistinguishable from any of the dozens shuffling into the unit at visiting time to keep loyal vigil at the bedside of their fading spouse. *He could be English!* Her mind moves unbidden to the small flat she shares with Steve in the multi-rise east London council estate. The fear-drenched walkways with their crude decorations of swastikas and other fascist symbols. The many times she has been kicked and spat on. White faces twisting into masks of hate, screaming obscenities at her because her skin is black. She thinks about the filth and slogans scrawled across the entrance to her flat, the bucket full of water she keeps behind the front door to catch the burning rags stuffed through the letterbox most nights.

A vision of herself growing old in that landscape comes unbidden to her mind. Anguish knifes its way through her belly. It brings resentment against this old man, foreign like herself, yet so at home in this unfamiliar place. The old man continues to stare expectantly at her. Lena ignores him. She attempts to sidle away, pretending his words are aimed at other ears in the empty landscape.

'Excuse me.' He refuses to allow her polite escape. 'You work here, don't you?'

She offers him her remote smile, professional politeness claiming distance as she checks her watch face to underline the message of a busy life. 'Yes.'

He shuffles closer to the tree in unconscious challenge, refusing to be deterred. 'The wife,' he persists, 'loved that tree . . . planted it in '32, seven years before the great war. Guess it was on account of the one my parents had. Dad was always saying how much it reminded him of the old country. It was the first thing he ever planted once he and Mother got a place of their own.'

The longing in the rusty voice finds echoes in her own mind. It catches her attention, setting her to unconscious forward motion. Close up he smells musty and stale as if unaccustomed to outdoor air.

'The wife,' he continues doggedly, 'she's been in here six weeks now. Don't think she gonna make it this time round. I think that's why no one wants to talk to me.' His voice trails off into the silence as his eyes shift back to the tree.

Lena's attention follows his. She too has left a tree behind. The hunger for a tree, any tree, even a tree like this to call her own is stronger than before. The constant drone of the bypass traffic fades into the distance as his finger traces the memory of another tree. The tree planted with his wife, perhaps even his father's tree planted in defiance so many lifetimes ago.

Her tree is citrus that yields warm sweet oranges. Planted with her navel string, nurtured by that thread which long ago attached her to her mother. It haunts her sleepless nights, calling her home in vain. Lena feels a sudden kinship with the rumpled old man. It softens her resentment at his rightness in this landscape which so cruelly underlines how out of place she feels. Aloofness gives way to curiosity about the history which brought an old American and his wife to this obscure part of south London.

He says his name is Petrosky but he does not want to talk about his family, beyond the fact that his parents emigrated from Poland to the USA during the great European wave at the end of the last century. That his mother never settled in the States and he, her last-born child, inherited her need to return and live in the old world. That the great war had put paid to plans to visit Poland and his wife had been too sick when Communism ended.

What he wants to talk about is the fears he has about his wife. He needs reassurance that this is not the end of the line for her. He wants to take her home because at their age death is always so close and he doesn't want to waste their remaining time together. He has been badgering her doctors, but since she was admitted six weeks before he hasn't received a single useful answer.

They have been together for nearly seventy years, sixty of them in England, and this is the first time since the war they have been parted so long. Today is the anniversary of her diagnosis with multiple sclerosis twenty-six years ago and he wants reassurance that she will go into remission as she had in the past.

Lena vaguely remembers the frail old woman with the shock of white hair, lying pale and still beneath the covers of the narrow hospital bed and has to think hard before the picture is focused in her mind. She can hear the registrar's impersonal voice droning through the old lady's prognosis at the last three ward rounds she attended. The consultant's acid humour when he commented on the way 'the old dear' was still clinging on to life.

Mrs Petrosky trapped inside the useless shell of her body, no longer even able to breathe by herself. Age, disease and twenty-six years of fighting the relentless progress of creeping paralysis has worn away the muscles of her heart and her mind is already fading.

Lena looks at the tarnished old man, whose age-wasted body no longer fits the contours of the old-fashioned double breasted suit. She shifts uneasily when she meets his steady gaze, reading the knowledge of his wife's impending death in the sad grey eyes. Lena turns abruptly to gaze at the city haze, afraid he will see her sudden guilty envy of what he shared with the dying woman.

Petrosky shifts unsteadily. She feels his gaze, feels him willing her to turn and reassure him. Words form in her head, congeal on her tongue. An image of Steve arises unbidden in her head. The bleak landscape of her marriage mocks her ability to understand his pain. It feels wrong somehow, to offer hollow comfort from her store of platitudes built up over the last two barren years. The anger returns abruptly, feeding the bitter jealousy, and she turns and walks away before it rains down on the old man's fragile form.

It's late afternoon by the time she gets back to her office. The workman and his transistor are long gone and the noise from the construction site has abated in the teatime lull. Lena returns her identity card to the windowledge and takes her own small radio from her desk drawer. Her fingers fiddle with the knob until she's tuned in to the afternoon cricket commentary, but her mind is no longer on the game.

She tries to focus on the file still open on her desk. Dave Miller – another patient with multiple sclerosis. Tall, blond, a bright twenty-one-year-old. Dave was diagnosed less than two years ago. He started dying inside his head the minute the scan discovered the platelets forming there. Dave's legs gave way first – after his will to lead a normal life – after he sold his car and his mother bought him a specially adapted vehicle. After he became a problem when his parents saw his bright future disappearing into a reversion to dependency.

The clock on the wall shows ten minutes to four and her working day finishes at five. A familiar apprehension starts deep inside her stomach as she contemplate the daily scramble to reach home before Steve does.

She was late on Monday. Lena flinches with the memory, hand going automatically to the healing bruise on her left cheek hidden under several layers of foundation. Steve laid into her the minute she closed the door, accusing her of seeing another man behind his back as he punched and kicked her to a grovelling, pleading mess. Afterwards, as she pulled her shivering body up the stairs, she could only be thankful that this time he had not cracked her ribs again.

Lena wraps her arms around herself in a futile attempt at comfort, feeling chilled and lonely despite the summer heat. Her mind wanders back to the old man under the mulberry tree. Mr Petrosky still loyal to his wife after seventy years. She thinks of her own four years of marriage, the fear that haunts her nights and stalks her weekend hours. She thinks of Mrs Petrosky living twenty-six years with multiple sclerosis, Dave Miller dying in two years from the same condition.

The warm summer afternoon is suddenly laden with the heavy scent of citrus, children's laughter carrying far across the clear air. The twisted lines of the ancient mulberry tree change shape inside her head, as the radio announcer heralds the end of her working day. Lena looks at the clock on the wall in dismay, the smell of sun-ripened oranges fading back into memory. Her mind lingers on the frail old woman dying in her narrow hospital bed after seventy years of loving and she wonders how much longer she can live with fear.

Oh Buddha

Jan Lo Shinebourne

She didn't know what to expect but it was disappointing to see that the clinic in Cricklewood was really just an ordinary house, not all that nice. It needed a good painting and the plants outside didn't look healthy either.

The woman who opened the door looked Italian or Greek, like Mrs Romani in Ridley Road. All this time, she was expecting an Englishwoman because her voice was so posh on the phone.

'Hello Sylvia,' she said, 'come in.' Her voice sounded more friendly but her face was serious.

The carpet and the wallpaper in the hall needed changing. Business couldn't be good if she couldn't afford to do up the place.

'Take off your coat and leave it here. Take off your shoes too, then come into the front room. We've started.'

She pointed to the back of the hall. It was full of coats thrown across the chairs and desk, and boots and shoes on the floor. Why did they have to take off their shoes? And why with so many people here was the place so quiet?

She took off her coat and shoes and followed the therapist into the front room where only women, no men, were sitting in a circle on the floor.

'I don't know if I can manage to sit on the floor,' she declared.

The therapist frowned and her friendly face changed quickly into an angry face, then changed back quickly into a serious face. 'You can bring one of the chairs in,' she said.

But now she didn't want to be the odd one out, so she said 'It's OK I'll try out the floor, only I'm not used to it. It makes me feel like a small child again.'

The therapist smiled a different kind of smile, a knowing smile. This way she had of changing her voice and her facial expressions one after another was really disturbing.

All the women were young.

'We're just doing our round, introducing ourselves,' the therapist explained, then she smiled, and nodded at one of the women.

This woman said, 'I'm Margaret. I've come a long way tonight, from Hackney. On the way here I felt very nervous about starting group therapy. I almost turned back because I was so nervous, and I'm still feeling really nervous. I want to be in therapy to try and sort myself out. I am thirty-three and I still can't get on with my mother. She really, really upsets me and I felt it was time I did something about it. So I hope you can help.'

'Thank you, Margaret,' the therapist said.

The three women who spoke after Margaret talked about their problems. They all talked about trouble with their parents and their relationships with their partners and their worries about getting support in the group. By the time it came to her turn she was feeling very frightened, and annoyed with herself for being frightened. After all, they were all women together and that was the time when you could talk about men and problems with them freely. That was why she had come here, to talk about Charley and get some help sorting him out. He was getting so crotchety, with his head balding, and his paunch getting bigger and this and that fretting him and making her life miserable.

She found herself saying exactly all this, not using words like relationship and partner like the other women, just talking about Charley. She couldn't stop talking once she started and the therapist had to stop her. She said, 'I have to stop you, Sylvia.'

After this, the therapist made them play a game. They had to take turns at being blindfolded and led around the flat by a partner. They had to choose this partner by instinct, by looking at each other. If the other person nodded, that was the sign that she wanted to be your partner. This choosing took a long time. She was going to wait for someone to choose her but got fed up and just nodded when she felt like it and the other woman nodded back, so they started before everyone else. The blindfolded person had to learn to trust her partner to lead her round the room, giving her various objects to touch and handle, let her feed her bits of food the therapist had left lying around. She had no trouble with this game, she didn't feel afraid or nervous as the therapist suggested they might feel. But she felt fed up with it because all she wanted to do was talk about Charley and get some advice with sorting him out.

After this they had to do a feedback round, with everyone saying how they felt doing the trust exercise. When it came to her turn, she said she found it boring and just wanted to get on with getting some advice about dealing with Charley. She said too that she did not have trouble with her mother. In fact she wished her mother was here instead of in Guyana because she would sort out Charley for her.

When this round was over, the therapist made a little speech. She talked about how difficult women found it to make time for themselves, how guilty they felt about it, how they were used to giving and not receiving, how hard they found it to be assertive. She said that their time here with her was time just for themselves to learn to use to get what they needed, to empower them. She said it was important for everyone to feel able to have trust in the group. There were rules: no violence, no drugs and no sex in the group. Then she said they had to finish in ten minutes but could use the time up doing a final round, and this she called the resentment round. She wanted everyone to express any resentments they experienced during the session. She asked Sylvia to start, and she said she felt the hour had been a disappointment because she came for some advice about how to handle Charley and didn't get it, so she was going home feeling disappointed.

The other women had no resentment, but when it came to the therapist's turn she looked straight at her and put on her angry face. She said to her, 'Sylvia I felt very resentful of you for several reasons. You have done nothing but complain throughout the session, about having to sit on the floor at the start, but mainly you were having a power struggle with me continually. I also resented you touching Margaret because she was crying. You were invading her space . . . '

She felt herself getting very angry. 'I only touch her to comfort her. Don't talk nonsense to me, for God's sake . . . '

One of the other women, Carol, put her hand up and said she wanted to express a resentment after all. The therapist gave her permission. Carol said, 'I am a Christian and I resent you Sylvia for taking God's name in vain. I don't feel I could be in a group with someone who did not respect God.'

'Oh God!' she cried out, totally fed up, and got up to leave. She had had enough. 'I didn't know this was a church group. If I wanted to be in a church group, I would go to church. And let me tell you when I say "Oh God" it is not a sign of disrespect. I am asking God for help!'

The therapist was smiling now and this was making Sylvia feel really angry. 'Anyway, I won't be coming back here since I am not wanted.'

Now the therapist put on her kind face and said, 'Please don't go, Sylvia, we do want you here. Sit down and let us work through the fear of rejection and anger you brought here with you. Maybe you need a round for yourself. Why don't you go round and ask everyone how they feel about having you here?'

'What for? This one, Carol, said she didn't want me because I call on God.'

Carol complained: 'You were abusing God. When you say "Oh God" you are abusing God.'

The therapist, still smiling, said, 'I tell you what, Sylvia and Carol, let's sort it out this way. Let's agree not to say "Oh God!" but "Oh Buddha!" instead. Then nobody can be offended.'

That was it. Sylvia had no doubt she didn't want to stay in this group. She went to put on her coat but the therapist followed her, and asked her to return and work on her anger with the group.

'You work on your own anger,' she said, and left.

Sweet Rice

Aamer Hussein

For Yasmien Abbasi
Who suggested a final, vital ingredient

A few weeks after her fortieth birthday (unremembered, unsung), Shireen underwent a brief crisis and then received an unexpected gift. This is how it happened:

Jamil, her husband – one of those dedicated bankers who spent his life between his office, his associates, his business trips and his bed – announced to her one Sunday from the shallows of early morning sleep that he had important people visiting from abroad and others to whom he desperately owed a seasonal invitation. In short, she had to cater for more than a dozen guests at less than a week's notice. The dinner was to be next Saturday, Shireen grumbled silently as she lowered herself deeper into the depths of Capricornian gloom, and she knew she would have to excel herself, for even her best was never good enough for Jamil's Libran discernment.

And so it had always been. Her medical expertise – so many years, and so much of her widowed mother's savings spent on it – had been displaced, in this impossibly difficult city of London where even a powerfully situated husband did not guarantee a work permit or a job for a doctor with a third world (read by the British as third-class) degree and experience, by an ongoing culinary struggle to keep her husband tied to her table, with sundry colleagues (for deals meant more to him than domestic life) in tow.

Such was life. Take Timur – now seven, and growing away from his mother – to school; do the shopping at Safeway and Marks and Spencer's on Edgware Road; go to Marylebone library for some Han Suyin books in which other Asian lands far from her own were reflected in a doctor's eyes; come home and desultorily clean up. (She'd dispensed with the idea of an au pair a while ago, for she needed something besides shopping to fill up the time that reminded her of the globe of her days which was filling up with sand, taking her further and further away from any chance of regaining her fine hospital job in Karachi, or of adding to her qualifications the required British degrees, for Jamil had always found some excuse: Timur was too little and medical training here expensive, and then he didn't know how long this English stay, sojourn for her and idyll for him, was going to last. And now a Malaysian woman, who was now more a friend than a cleaner, came in once a week to do what Jamil called the heavy jobs.) Then she'd cook for Jamil and his guests as well, for this, too, she insisted upon, though he'd lately suggested they order food from one of the fancy Pakistani lady caterers who were now proliferating in London, because once she'd said in irritation that she hadn't been brought up to cook for armies when he sprang a dinner on her, and now he thought her home cooking wasn't quite fancy enough for his guests though he thrived on it himself. But she wasn't going to subscribe to his theory of two weights and two measures – more than good enough for him but not for outsiders – and refused even to consider food from elsewhere. This, he claimed in contradiction to his earlier protests about her elitist disdain for polite feminine values, was due to what he called her elemsee upbringing . . . And once she'd seen a poster for an orchestra called LMC and wondered aloud why an orchestra would name itself Lower Middle Class until her friend Yasmien with whom she was walking down High Street Kensington shoved her in the ribs and said no, silly, that's a typically Pakistani term. LMC stands for the London Musicians' Collective . . . one did still laugh with one's friends sometimes. Usually, though, when Jamil wasn't here. And that was more and more often. Then she'd follow her daily routine with the addition of a visit or a walk with one of her two close friends, and come home and still persist in cooking, against modern dietary prescriptions, the dishes she loved like spinach with meat or potatoes, oil-rich courgettes and aubergines, rich buttery breads and dry, fragrant pea-speckled rice tinted yellow. Since that was the role she'd been allotted by life's scene-shifters, she'd be a housewife with all the perfectionism of her medical training. But all too often she couldn't eat alone, and her friends were occupied with their matrimonial tasks, so she'd freeze the food for some day when it rained or snowed. Then, in her favourite armchair, late into the night, she'd read and reread the stories of Han Suyin's life among the women of China and Malaya.

Now, this party. Jamil had gone off to Brussels on Monday morning, flying from the City Airport which he found most convenient for flights to Europe (but all too often it was to the Asia-Pacific region he went, for that, he said, was where the economy was booming, and other Asians, too, should make sure of their slice of the cake). Though Shireen dreaded those guests of his – this time there'd be some from Asia-Pacific and America – with their wives who looked suspiciously at the clothes she'd had sent to her from Pakistan and snooped around her fixtures and fittings, she was determined to prepare something really special, and outdo those society hostesses whose homes he dragged her to every sixth week or so when he was here. She'd already run through her repertoire of homely fare – after all, as a medical student and then a practitioner, she'd hardly had time to acquire the skills of her family's women: some passive knowledge, some pragmatic tips and some inherited skills had so far sufficed. But now, with the frustrated and frustrating perfectionism that constantly chilled her bones, she wanted to cross the final boundary and cook one of the feasts she'd heard her grandmother describe with such chop-licking ecstasy.

Sweet rice. A delicacy remembered from the day she'd kept all her Ramadan fasts for the first time. Not the insipid sweet yellow stuff speckled with shaved nuts, but something lush and golden orange, laden with succulent pieces of chicken and ripe with the subtle and suggestive perfume of fruit. Grandmother had made it for her and named it – or so, in her eight-year-old's arrogance, she'd imagined – after her. Shireen pulao. Sweet rice.

Shireen's father was from the Punjab, but her mother's parents – as they'd loved to remind her – had come from some small town in what were now the United Provinces in Northern India. They'd settled in Lahore many years before Partition, but retained the gentle gestures, the sweet tongues and the richly aromatic cooking of another era, another land. After 1947 the landholdings which had given them a small revenue and some claim to feudal graces had vanished – and unlike many others, they'd never applied for recompense, which would have been a futile endeavour, as those who complained of properties lost were so many and there just didn't seem to be enough to go around. Her grandfather had lived all his life on his physician's earnings, and her father, too, was a doctor: simple people, who'd fallen in a world that continued to respect material manifestations of heritage, but hardly elemsee as Jamil put it. That, she thought in catty moods, suited him better; and what was worse, his family had the mentality of shopkeepers with new money. But that was the way things were these days in Pakistan . . .

Enough reminiscing for now, she thought as she turned the corner from Seymour Place into York Street, which led her home (above her, the inverted grey tin bowl of sky). Grandmother was no longer there, and Mother had probably long since forgotten a recipe of such absurdly luxurious pretensions. Now where could she find it? Hardly any chance of recovering it from the exercise books filled up with recipes her mother had copied out in her arthritic hand, or Shireen had painstakingly translated or transcribed – her Urdu, so fluent when she was younger, had grown almost rusty from years of disuse (medical textbooks in

Urdu? Don't make me laugh. They're written in untranslatable gibberish.) Then there were the volumes of Madhur Jaffrey cookbooks that Jamil had brought for her, probably as a burdensome hint – they'd been placed by her on a corridor shelf and proudly forgotten; though friends had told her the recipes within them were authentic, timesaving and good, the vanity of a good daughter, rich in the dowry of a thousand recipes tested and proved, forbade her to turn to them. Once upstairs, in the comfortable sitting room of her flat, feet tucked up beneath her in a favourite pudgy armchair, she swallowed her lumpy, irksome pride; a pile of discarded notebooks beside her, she inspected Jaffrey's heavy tomes as if in search of some obscure remedy in a respected encyclopaedia. But to no avail. What would she do? Her goat-like determination refused to allow her to give up. Sweet rice. It would have been a gesture so grand, so uncharacteristically flamboyant, a celebration of her home, and above all a defiant signature (named after her, the sweet rice, the indulgent grandmother had deceitfully said, the indulged child had gullibly believed) . . . What have I ever signed with a flourish, Shireen said to herself. Do I even remember my signature, and this son of mine is his father's child, an English child, who prefers dubiously prepared hamburgers and chips fried in the greasy remains of God knows what forbidden animal to his mother's healthy cooking; give him a fresh, sweet lassi and he asks for an artificially flavoured yoghurt . . .

Then a picture teased her visual memory. She went to the hall cupboard – in use this season, as their coats and winter things were stored there – and retrieved a chest in which some ancient objects of sentimental value (don't look back and above all don't smell or sniff, it only takes you to places surrendered) were stored. She knelt there on the carpet, rummaging, foraging. A red scarf. Two saris. And the bundle of books. They tumbled out – first those novels of A.R. Khatoon that had delighted her between the ages of twelve and fifteen: 'chaste, pragmatic romances', as a Frontier Post columnist, Shahnaz Aijazuddin – who'd recently written about the creative apathy of Western-educated Pakistani women, too – had described them, in a fulsome tone that amazed her because, as a teenager, she'd finally, regretfully relegated them to a corner, submitting to the senior schoolchild's unwritten law of Westernisation which decreed that anything local or ethnic, except the odd piece of mystic music, was suspect, unworthy, elemsee, while English was chic and desirable. Then, some romances of Islam and of colonialism and the '57 uprising by Abdul Halim Sharar, whom the Urdu scholars of today considered as dated as Rider Haggard. Here, now. The classic book of recipes she'd been searching for.

She'd taken the bundle of books from her grandmother's cupboard when the old lady died, aged eighty-three; a sentimental gesture, followed by the contradictory, even furtive, action of hiding them, once she'd carted them to London, under piles of gauzy unusable garments behind her husband's sports gear and her son's array of sundry school things. A moth-eaten, mildewed book. The Urdu script was old-fashionedly pure and clear, faint now with time but still legible. The title page stated the year of publication – 1911 – and the title. *Naimatkhana*, it was called – the traditional larder. She had never, when she took it away, imagined she'd have use for it in these labour-saving days, and even the names, weights and terms in it, as she browsed, were archaic. But – after a false and disappointing start, since it wasn't included in the book's list of contents and she couldn't locate a familiar heading – the recipe appeared. On page 89.

Orange rice, the author had called it. Chicken or lamb, rice, clarified butter, onions, coriander, garlic, salt, cumin, black pepper, cloves, cardamom and sugar. And then, for the remembered fragrance (heady, like playing the circle game with your favourite boy cousin in the sun), she had to turn to recipe no. 249, on page 192. A sauce of orange peel, almonds, pistachios, cardamoms, water and – for the final, special, touch – crystallised rock sugar. All ingredients so easy to find, nowadays, in this city that had no cuisine of its own to boast of; which had, in its usual, grudging and offhand way, taken to guzzling the delicacies of its erstwhile empire and was even developing an increasingly discerning palate for them. Little Asias of restaurants and eating places had taken over the city – the revenge of the spice islands, as she and Yasmien jokingly said when they chose places to shop and eat. The rock sugar, perhaps, would be difficult to locate – but Drummond Street, for a sturdy walker like her (she walked for hours in post-autumnal, leaf-bare Regent's Park sometimes), was only a short walk away, though she hated its dinginess and its stalely spicy smells. And if not, then Harrods or Fortnums would be sure to stock it . . . In the end, she'd have gone even beyond the remembered delight to create something new, something lavish and wonderful, a festive concoction that bore her name . . .

Later, though. For now – Jamil always said, when he saw the increasing pile, in her usually orderly surroundings, of medical digests and newspapers, imported *Heralds*, *Shes*, and *Frontier Posts*, free handouts, *Big Issues*, and mail-order catalogues she saved because there was always something she wanted to read again, that Shireen would even find something to devour with her eyes on the back of a cereal pack, an airline ticket or a postage stamp. It was a joke she was sure he'd picked up from one of the American men's magazines that were his only leisure reading, or from an in-flight journal, this tasteless description of the kind of passionate, indefatigable reader she was – for now she had found a companion: the book would keep her engrossed, amused, transported, for hours.

When she reached the last of the recipes (homesickness sometimes is closer than anything to happiness) she still had half an hour before she left to pick up Timur, who she'd remembered had football practice after classes today, from his school near Marble Arch. She discovered an index of recipes at the end of the book; no point now in regretting that she hadn't located it earlier, for half the fun of finding the recipe for sweet rice had been the search for it. Beyond the index was a list of books published by the same house. She realised that they were all by the author of this book, whom she'd imagined as a semi-literate bourgeoise, a turn-of-the-century housewife. Her ignorance astonished her, for this woman, Muhammadi Begum, had been the editor of the first influential Urdu journal for women, which her husband had founded in Lahore in 1898. She had written at least a dozen books in the span of just ten years. Some were guides to housekeeping and good manners, but the titles of others, and the short, pithy blurbs below, made her long for a grand library. A book for children: a young girl seeks a magic fountain, tree and bird to free her brothers from captivity; they have turned to stone. (Will Jamil, too, free his limbs one day, from their pervasive torpor?) A tale for adolescents: a poor but highly learned young girl works day and night, setting up a school for girls, using her intelligence and wits to pay for her brother's schooling and her mother's recovery from mental illness. (And here I complain, listless.) Two novels for adults: one about the evils of forcing an educated young woman – interested in the study of medicine and the art of herbalism – to marry her incompetent, dissipated cousin, and driving her to despair and death. (And what have I done? Jamil was not my cousin, but I didn't love him, and settled for a marriage of convenience because my work didn't give me time and I was afraid and over thirty.) A biography: of a role-model, an impoverished widow who'd become the principal of a vernacular girls' school in colonial Lahore, well over a century ago.

Who was this writer, then, this master cook who'd stirred the ingredients of romance and realism into platters of parables that had nurtured generations of women, secluded or newly emergent from the confines of four walls and veils, adding a special prescription for those women who, almost a century later, were doctors and lawyers and opposition leaders and even prime ministers. Muhammadi Begum had died – so the prefaces, written by her stepdaughter and stepdaughter-in-law told Shireen – in 1908 at the age of thirty (and I am already forty, and still alive, and have abandoned my years of useful training and service to languish and moan in a luxurious central London flat), finding time to leave behind this keepsake of herself, this cookery book, the only work for which she was remembered, by a multitude of women who continued to share her bounty (and sharing bread is the closest form of love), taken from this *Naimatkhana* she left behind her?

Naimatkhana. Simply translated, a larder or storehouse. Literally, a house or chamber of bounty. And it was from this chamber of bounty or blessings that Shireen would draw sustenance. She would share what she had, give unstintingly, take what was offered, laid out out on the *dastarkhan*, the fresh white banqueting tablecloth of life. All the way to Timur's school, she pondered, she brooded: yes, the dish that bore her own name, that she would prepare; but she'd do much more. She'd go to the India Office library and excavate, reclaim whichever of Muhammadi Begum's writings she could find; she'd spend her remaining fallow years in this foreign country recreating a forgotten time from her own past, giving back to this amazing woman – of whom no photograph existed for, as a traditional Muslim woman, she had never forsaken her purdah – her purloined history.

On her way home, holding Timur's unwilling hand in the bus (like his father, the child didn't like to walk), Shireen paid little attention to the child's customary pampered nonsense. Like Shireen's own father, Muhammadi Begum's husband Mumtaz Ali had encouraged her endeavours – a radical religious scholar, he had fought for the rights of women to choose their own destinies, to emerge into the light of education and the dignity of unveiling, to marry and to divorce whom they chose, to walk and work in the world as men's equals. Recognising her superior talent, he had set up a press for his teenage wife, published her books, and kept them and her memory alive for many, many years after her death . . . (and will Jamil think of me when I go? Has living abroad pushed him back into some realm of the colonised, the spineless who fear the vocal freedom of their equals and partners, as the ruler fears the mocking songs of his subjects? Does this city allow freedom only to those that fill its treasuries with borrowed or stolen pounds? Who will support me if I spend years researching the life of a woman whose potent writings, by a trick of history and idle conversation, are probably interred in the mildewed and mite-infested coffers of empire?)

Shireen had decided. When she'd finally settled Timur in front of one of his interminable Mario games – a special favour, on a weekday – she picked up the phone and dialled Yasmien's number. Yasmien's machine switched itself on. Resignedly, Shireen said: 'Call me when you can, it's nothing important – Well, actually, I wondered if you and your husband are free on Saturday, for dinner . . . '

'My husband's not here,' Yasmien's voice interrupted her, 'and I'm free all week. Sorry about the machine. I was avoiding Tehmina, you know how long she goes on . . . '

'Listen, I'm thinking of compiling a recipe book. You know, based on those recipes from our grandmothers' time? I'm thinking of calling it *Sweet Rice*.'

Half an hour later (or maybe two hours, for she hadn't looked at her watch when she called Yasmien, and they'd traversed a century and more in their conversation) she had a collaborator, a fellow conspirator. Yasmien knew of someone who knew a publisher in Pakistan, who might later be interested in assisting Shireen in her project of writing about her new heroine's life. With the fashionable status of Asian food in Britain, they'd have no major problem in finding an outlet here for *Sweet Rice*. The fancy Pakistani lady caterers, once they'd wept their kohl in streams down their faces, would throng to the spectacular launch, and later claim the recipes they'd copy had originated in their mothers' kitchens. And Yasmien had suggested a subtitle, and a vital ingredient for their Bountiful Feast: there'd be lots of bright illustrations, and between the recipes, to refresh the palate like cool sweet water, they'd serve whatever stories they could uncover of the life of Muhammdi Begum, and as condiments they could recount their own experiences of living and cooking at home and in alien lands.

Muhammadi Begum (1878–1908), editor of *Tehzeeb-i-Niswan* and the mother of Urdu fiction, is not a fictional character. I have in my possession some volumes of her essays and marvellously anti-romantic romances, and I recently unearthed in London, as a gift for my mother, a copy of *Naimatkhana*, in its eleventh edition by 1960.

The White Spring

Zinovy Zinik

After her two-year stay in Moscow, Clea – ex-Trotskyite and militant vegetarian – has returned to London with her Russian husband, Konstantin, only to witness a complete transformation in his personality. In Moscow he was known for his obsession with Western cuisine. In England his eccentricity has taken a U-turn. He is a sub-species of homo sovieticus, *incapable of fitting into any culture, an alien at home and abroad.*

It was no coincidence that Kostya had begun to hold forth about the Tartar khans and samovars, for he had started to behave like a Tartar himself. At her first appearance with Kostya in public, Clea realised that the creature she had brought to London was an Asiatic with a greedy, slit-eyed look. The reception or, as the English call it, 'the party' in honour of their arrival on the shores of Albion, had been arranged on Margot's initiative and held in Anthony's elegant flat in Kensington. Clea had hated the whole idea from the start; she hated Anthony's new flat for its trendy bareness, its glossy and expensive fittings, its open fireplaces and its bar. She had guessed in advance, when Anthony was showing them round the flat, that he would casually draw their attention to a brass candlestick, bought for a fortune in the Portobello Road, stressing that he had bought it in a flea market, as if no one knew that it had long since ceased to be a 'flea market' and was now a collection of smart antique shops for rich eccentrics and tourists; that he would complain about his neighbour, an 'oil magnate from the sands of Arabia', one of those *noveau riche* Arabs who were buying up the best houses in London with the result (hypocritical sigh) that ordinary citizens were unable to find a decent, modest place to live because the price of property had been so inflated; that he would say: 'Margot and I decided not to carpet the floors but just to leave them as they are – it's so much nicer and simpler without carpets,' although any fool knew what a fortune it cost to sand and polish these oaken woodblock floors – his guests could see themselves reflected from head to foot, simply in order to be reminded of their own insignificance; that he would casually straighten in passing a nineteenth-century engraving that depicted a coal mine complete with Victorian winding-gear, saying as he did so: 'Look – the coalminer's lot hasn't changed since Dickens' time, has it? Ah, the horror of it! With ice or without?'

She had also detested the prospect of a crowd of her girlfriends from university days, whom she had not seen for years; they would all, she knew, come running for the opportunity to peck her on the cheek and then to go into idiotic raptures about this happy solution to her peculiar and difficult ordeal in Russia, whereupon they would whisper to each other in a corner about this absurd foreigner, this Asiatic Tartar whom she had dug out of some Russian garbage-tip for lack of other matrimonial alternatives.

All this, of course, was beyond the reach of Kostya's understanding. Like any newcomer, it was doubtful whether he understood the difference between fashionable Kensington and humble Kennington, just as he was unable to appreciate the difference between cheap carpets and varnished parquet – indeed he perceived it in exactly reverse terms, regarding carpets as smarter because in Moscow one had to queue for them whole days and nights, whereas everyone there had parquet floors even if they were not quite of the same quality.

He was, however, amazed at the variety of drinks and, above all, by the way they were served: from a bar-counter, where there was even draught beer in a barrel that was delivered to one's home. This touched him. For the rest, he understood little – who these people were, why they had come and what they were talking about. When questioned, he would mumble a vague reply, grinning politely, nodding in answer to a nod, smiling in response to a smile – in the way that every foreigner, to be on the safe side, apes the grimaces of his interlocutor when he understands neither the language nor the customs of the natives.

Defeated in their attempts to extract from Kostya an analysis of the difference between totalitarianism and democracy, the guests finally left him alone. Clutching a large mug of beer, he settled himself comfortably in a corner on some large cushions against the wall, which were even more pleasant than an armchair, and where he was finally able truly to relax after all the problems and rows induced by leaving Moscow and travelling to England, accompanied as it had been by a permanent chorus of advisers and inquisitive onlookers. A forest of English legs flickered in front of him as the guests danced away their 'party'. These 'party members', as he mentally dubbed them, were also drinking beer, but in a strange way – without eating anything, as Russians do, and if they did eat as they drank then only roast peanuts; in other words, they were eating something sweetish, whereas it was obvious to anyone that beer needed something salty to stimulate one's thirst, so that one could then satisfactorily quench that thirst by pouring a deep draught of beer down one's throat. But Kostya was in luck: alongside the cushions he found an elegant little stool made of some obviously precious kind of wood, and on that graceful piece of furniture was an equally graceful china saucer, upon which, in pleasant if disorderly profusion, someone had poured a heap of small black rusks. The rusk-bearing stool was thoughtfully placed at such a height that anyone reclining on the cushions had only to stretch out a hand to pick up a supply of rusks without even looking. And the rusks turned out to be exactly what was wanted: salty, but not too much so, just right for this light beer that the guests for some reason called by the Russian word for 'prison camp' – *lager* – apparently in Kostya's honour.

Kostya luxuriated in his corner on the cushions, sipping his beer and nibbling rusks. It was a good thing that Margot and Anthony had been to Moscow – they obviously knew the proper way to drink beer. Anthony, however, in passing by, stopped and raised his eyebrows in astonishment. Pointing to the rusks he enquired hesitantly: 'Er . . . do you like them?' To which Kostya hastened to explain how one's gullet was stimulated by provoking thirst with something slightly salty when one was drinking beer. Anthony obviously had trouble in understanding Kostya's little discourse and moved away with an odd sort of smile, shrugging his shoulders. And he was not the only one. Kostya noticed that many of the guests were glancing round and giving him amazed looks; some were obviously trying to push their way over to his cushion-filled corner, and having seen for themselves that Kostya really was eating these rusks as he drank his beer, would go away again, hiding embarrassed smiles behind their hands. Clearly the Russian way of drinking beer struck these islanders as comical and absurd – although it was of course possible that these curious onlookers had simply walked over to stare at Kostya himself, a specimen of *homo sovieticus* in an English zoo. Finally it dawned on him that maybe he was not alone in liking these delicious little rusks, but that everyone was too shy to say so and they were all amazed at the obtuseness of this Russian who was monopolising the whole bowlful of this rare delicacy.

Such was indeed the case, to judge by the look of dismay on Clea's face, who was pushing her way through the crowd of guests, making enigmatic warning signs to Kostya from the other end of the room. Before this she had been circulating animatedly from one little group to another, and by the selection of words reaching Kostya's ears, such as 'politburo', '*Pravda*' and '*apparatchik*', she had been kindly describing to the guests the horrors of totalitarianism and the Soviet censorship. Now, though, her face was distorted in a spasm of disgust. Reaching Kostya's corner, she pointed at the china bowl and hissed in his ear: 'Do you think those were put there for you? Why are you eating them?' Since Clea could not be suspected of ignorance of Russian beer-drinking rituals, she was obviously accusing Kostya of having cornered these rusks for himself and refusing to share them with others. 'Why are you behaving like such a clown?' she went on, shaking with fury. The matter was obviously more serious than Kostya had supposed. 'Are you trying to make me into a laughing-stock? Don't you realise who those rusks are meant for?' Kostya did not realise; but at that moment the answer provided itself: with a tinkle of the little bell fastened to its collar, a huge ginger tom-cat jumped up on to Kostya's knees, bent its well-fed face towards the little stool and began systematically to devour the rusks in the china bowl, glancing around hungrily and licking its chops.

'Why didn't anybody tell me it was the cat's bowl?' Kostya muttered in a hurt voice as Clea was taking him to the bus-stop.

'Why? Because this is not the Soviet Union!' snapped Clea. 'This is a free country. You can eat dog-shit if you like and no one will say a word to you – especially since, as far as the English know, that's what the Russian population eats anyway.'

Pomegranates

Briar Wood

With a craving this persistent
I could be pregnant
but only want to conceive
a child. Waking to a breaking
wave of curved sunlight
waterlogged as flotsam.

These are the underground months.
It is just enough to ask
how to lose sight of dry land
in a history of daylight robbery.
When a cry for help might rebound
across the clearing clotted by violets
and what solitary witnesses tell
a mother who arrives too late
with ransacking of conscience.

The market-place rages.
Sound is a mouthful of teeth.
Biting a handgrenade.
Swallowing more than can be chewed.
Jewelled cruelties. Spilling their guts.

Ineluctable. The word for more
rolling snugly on the tongue.
Blood from a stone.

Fork out for a pound or two
of hell fruit. Smouldering coals.
Hugging a basket of answers.
Ruby fluid trickles in the fissure
where hearts have their compartments.
Frog spawn. Borne on the river ride.
Arteries beat. Clustered streets.

A View of Courtyards

Mimi Khalvati

As though a courtyard were the pedestal
of a column – set in stone –
of air and sunmotes, winter draughts
that, ambushed in its paths of light,
struck canopies and eaves
with gloom, with gold . . .

as though cornices and lintels,
                    parapets, window-jambs
etching shadow-teeth on terraces,
                    skiagraphs on brick,
were starclocks, sundials,
henges that were homes . . .

the way herdsmen move from slope to slope,
swallows wing from shelf to shelf

at the equinox they moved
lugging bedding, bundles, samovars
across the yard, past the pond
(holding heatwave safe behind their backs,
sunlight warm along their laps)

as the season turned
and the weaver's shadow
altered on the loom.

As sunrise spins itself in barberries,
dusk conceals in jams,
so kitchens faced the east
(for morning sun is good sun),
storerooms west
and in between, bicameral as the heart,
living room
changed hands.

My lover phones to say he's had enough of this
– this never knowing what the time is –
and has bought himself two clocks.

North and south still chiming in my head
the bond between us tightens

and here we are again – though miles apart –
bound in our parallels, as he sets
bells ringing, times
a coincidence of paths.

As though sherbert vials, waterjars
were to think of dust, downtown,
roads going south where the Gulf lies,
vacant, under defunct oil-rigs

(where the urchin's light green eyes
are of thinnest glass, frontages
only fronds could ever wave behind,
no homefire burn in . . .)

and the insistent phrase
in search of its outlet song
could not escape so wide a plain
or the flute breath's holding,

undoing what damage the old view did
I place myself at thresholds
– vernal, autumnal –

garden
where my heart is.

But – paths running parallel – solstice
came and with it another separation
and so I brought the garden table in,
wiped web and rust, lined it up
with a sill whose outer half,
dark in the shade of a rampant vine,
will later catch its raisins . . .

Seldom used it. Used
the stones of my yard so well
– lying under lavatera – they buckle
even more now, splinter, tip dangerously
on the very step where my mother fell,
fractured her pelvis – first
in a line of hairline cracks
becoming broken cradles . . .

Moved back in. To my old desk,
an upstairs view of the Archway Road,
next door's rose failing to get a grip
on lace, across the road, my neighbours.

Having lost the power to move at will,
not my own, but the seasons',
encumbered with belongings
as though fixtures and fittings
were my metaphor for roots,
I function where my habit is

far from rooms determined
by the gold along a wall,
the alchemy of ponds
turning memory of water
to ice and back to water,

tied as I am
by fear of loneliness to a man
whose contract with mobility
has shunted me off flightpaths,
passed me like a caravan.

Lacking southern sun
to leak from an unseen source
behind thicket, cloud or cornstack,
light to make it finite,

my shadow
is all ground on which I walk,
sky to which I turn,
no Mecca, no Jerusalem,

no weft or warp
in brickwork or basketry

to say I am, am not, I am.

Facing the Archway Road,
an older lifeline teases, thin
as a single hair but strong as fishing-line,
something going backwards
on an airpath between spine and door,
door and newel-post, that curlicues
the stairwell, exits into garden,
frazzles loose ends into air
that will snare them in illuminations,
the machinations of the zodiac.

Now love and light stored up in me
coincide with what went before,
before I lost my bearings,
coincidence of earth and sky,
past and future sibling grain
in our elders' sifting hands.

For divisions we have come to prise,
earth a house and garden we inhabit,
sky a bafflement of maths
despite moonwalks, space probes, sky labs,
they did not: saw themselves as underbelly
and sky a slender frame like Knut,
lid for sarcophagus and land.

As though an *eyvan*, meeting-point
of greeting, parting, veranda boards
over which a household trudged
or came to rest while an infant slept

were the locus of the soul
between the spirit that is garden,
body that is home

(where leg-bindings loosed
even as a journey ended
would let the heart go out,
the soul repair . . .)

I undress walls, pull
carpets back and forth
to redefine the focal point,

stoop to pick up mail.

Bedrooms were no battlefields,
no single parents' boxed retreats.
'Don't let the child sleep by herself!'
    the women warned
as though night were a stranger offering sweets.

But night was a sling of bedrolls
    flung this way, that way,
on terraces or carpets, wherever day had landed
childfalls, summer-calling cousins,
a bridegroom from the city

and bedrooms only latitudes
to give them bed and board
with every night a new – however fabulous –
configuration, ever redefining
what yesterday found fitting.

As for dining-rooms?
There was no such thing.
A tent, perhaps, in the orchard
of a house where you spent long summers,
remembered best its boiling vat,
globe of morning milk;

or the cooling length of a hallway
where the barest draughts slinked
in and out, reared at the door
as the cloth flared up
and rice came steaming in.

Spines that reached with ease for bread,
even the old, crosslegged,
thighbones lying flat on earth,
hipjoints opening down to earth
as though to help her
take them in.

As though, on some dazzling noon veranda,
an oil-lamp flame were left, like Cinderella,
still burning in its rags

every year the stars rise later,
emerge in half-light
when one's relation to the half-seen plants,
marrow under giant leaves, seems sacrosanct.

In a summer-house of six rooms,
in every room a fireplace, my mother
as a child scissored to their covings
cardboard floors, walls, interiors

she furnished with matchboxes, wire,
seashells, felt scraps; even
tiny rugs that bore, like exports,
the weave of a small girl's hand.

When inhabitants of the real rooms,
curling up on mattresses, in moments
before sleep, let their eyes fall
on sofas, bureaux, bedroom suites
any western home might have

it must have been as though
falling through a looking-glass
into daughters' lives where fires burn,
wood gleams, bedrooms where in every
nook and cranny is a turning in cocoons,
a learning and unlearning –

the past a cold stone fireplace,
oil-lamp with no wick,
journey into sand . . .

as though a doll's house with no dolls,
a dome within a dome
could have prophesied a shrinking world
where the soul mistakes
its yearning for migration
for freedom to cover earth's span;

even while furniture is being placed,
carpets tacked and the saw, screw,
unpartnering our seasons,
nailing down the flux,
the vagary of maps.

As though this loss, this giving away
of the shirt off one's back, discarding
a love that no longer fits

were only a pupal stage
and this flick of the pink, fireflash,
only fright coloration
before the moth takes wing,

with a click of the latch
I take to the bark,
fly my colours,

survive
on homegrounds wings can match.

Ham – is a Persian prefix meaning -mate,
so *hambazi* is a playmate,
hamclassi a classmate
and our word for neighbour
is *hamsayeh*, meaning
one who lives in the same shadow,
a shadow-mate.

A good word
is as a good tree –
its root set firm,
and its branches in heaven;
giving its fruit at every season
by the leave of its Lord.

I wish to learn the good words
in Gur'an or Bible,
in women's words or man's.

I wish to find their offspring,
the shadow-groupings in the fireplace,
this family or that *fameel,*
madar, pedar, dokhtar.

Learn how to set the future
newly bathed upon my lap,
bring sky down to wrap us in,
feel myself as human as I am.

Have David at his desk across the street,
Karen in her kitchen
feel as close as fist to fist on rope
or gazing up the starclock chute
as the tug on heel and hand.

Have skylight be to calendar
what soul should be to self

vision
to these small repeated acts.

Kurt Schwitters in Lakeland

Michael Hoffmann

'Like nothing else in Tennessee' – *Wallace Stevens*

It was between greens (bowling, cricket),
but the graveyard had stayed immune, half-cut, and
  smelling
the yellow, abandoned smell of hay. A couple were casting
dead flowers into a wire trash-coop.

Kurt Schwitters's tombstone was hewn in straight lines,
klipp und klar, in the shape of a hat, brim – crown.
Unseasonable, but undeniably local,
someone had left a dozen daffodils.

The man had flown: a refugee,
then interned on the Isle of Man;
released, dead, exhumed, and returned to Germany,
to vote with his feet for the 1950s.

His *Merz* was nothing to do with pain or March:
it had been withdrawn from the *Kommerz- und*
  Privatbank.
Each day he caught the early bus to work,
climbed up to his barn through a jungle of
  rhododendrons,

and built on to his *Merzwall.* – It too was moved,
cased in a steel frame, and keelhauled down the hill.
The one thing still there that his hands had touched
was a stone on the sill

of the picture window that had been put in
in place of the wall. It had an air
of having been given a spin,
a duck, a drakkar, a curling-stone.

One Never Knows

Kelvin Christopher James

It had been one of those intoxicating days winter grudgingly offers as reprieve after six grim weeks of blizzards, frost, and unrelenting cold. The sun had come out into pure blue skies and crystal-clear air. Now late afternoon, it still shone spiritedly through branches laden with last night's snowstorm. Nearer the earth, brilliant rays and shifting beams reflected from the snowdrifts, sparkling winks seducing me along the path.

Off and on, I passed other sunshine worshipers, strolling, playing, animating Christmas-card scenes. Shame all of it'd be too soon a memory: the gloam of evening close, the passing moments' pleasant reminder how winter begrudges but so much.

Up a slight but continuous incline led me to the knoll near the center of the park, and I was decidedly huffing it by the time I had trudged there. I should go on more, the heart needing just such deliberate stress to grow strong again. But doctor's orders or no, my bellows apparatus needed pause. So, the first bench at hand, I sat and gave my sturdy cane a rest, while I puffed my hip-hopping heart back to a foxtrot beat.

It was a tranquil spot presenting a pleasant panorama of the park. The gaze could linger on the blank flower plots near the front gates, on my exercise incline with its snow-blanketed pathways winding up through heavy-branched firs and pines.

The far end of the view found a thick, continuous green of well-forested hills, any of which'd be fine vantage to watch the moon rise, or the city's evening light up: a best window for any sort of busybody.

Nearer by, the parka-clad folks frolicking in the snowy flats were colorful teddy bears to me without my glasses. With puffs of breath, they semaphored fun to each other; word-clouds of closeness that remained afloat in their departed space.

All about, the air was alive with children – their keening screams, their snowballs, the delight of their laughter. They were romping and tumbling and frisking and falling in a manner that assured they'd all sleep well tonight.

Penetrating my musings, it slowly occurred to me that there was something odd about the person standing under a young fir some fifty feet away, at about three o'clock in my view. A family on their way out passed near him, and their little girl had to be called back from wandering over to interact with the stranger. But it was a casual recall by the parents. No tension at all. Still, my suspicious subconscious maintained scrutiny.

Abruptly, he sauntered on, and I recognised what was peculiar. He was a small man but didn't carry himself so. In fact, his stroll was more like a strut, albeit slope-shouldered and loping, which, with long hands thrust deep into his pockets, made him seem to be bouncing along with a presumptuous jauntiness.

I suddenly realised he had left the beaten snow of the pathways, and was plowing through the two-foot-deep lawns, heading directly toward me. Anxious that he had felt need to respond to my scrutiny and dreading a confrontation, I stared down at my feet in dismay.

When the effort of his excursion sounded near enough, I stole a glance up. My peek was immediately overcome by the eyes in his face: right on me, bright, alert, intensely examining. Still, my brief look could not miss the challenging gleams of intelligence crowning the vaguely triangular face. But by then he was quite close, so I retreated to lowered eyes once more, and reached into my pocket for the peanuts I had purchased on the way here.

Then, to my utter chagrin, the fellow took a seat at the other end of my bench.

Steadfastly, I gazed for lonely freedom through the broad window of my view as if his presence were a wall that separated our spaces. Although, of course, nothing he did escaped my wary side-minding of him. And, gradually, my puzzled observation became certain that his eyes and interest were only for the bag of peanuts I held.

For further evidence, I switched the bag to my right hand, away from his side. As if his stare were magnetised to it by a powerful beam, the fellow followed forward like a leaning pole to keep the bag in view. At that, I felt a melting within, and a trickle of guilt seeped out. For I had been biased to the face of strangeness. And even now, I was being selfish to the mouth of hunger. I couldn't have felt more ashamed. And, without daring to look his way, I offered the bag over.

He wasn't coy. There was no wait. The bag was swiftly from my hand. I heard the uncrimping as its wrapper yielded, the rattling of the roasted unshelled peanuts as they were scooped out. Then the bag was placed on the bench, and the evening was serene but for the urgent crackle of shells, and the rapid mouth-muffled crunch of peanuts.

From behind a pretended yawn, I sidled a glance down the bench and confirmed that the fellow had indeed placed the bag right next to his own leg, fully an arm's length away from me.

Now that I didn't like! Be he hungry or not, such was improper response to my generosity. My sympathy quickly diffused, unmasking the rudeness of his intrusion. Still, I was civilised; I did not snatch. Instead, eyes only on the bag, I leaned over, took it up, and scooped out two or three peanuts. Then I deliberately replaced the bag on the seat, halfway between us.

Didn't have to look to know he had followed my every move. His attention was a fixed stare I could feel, leaving me warm with embarrassment at my unsubtle parry. But I couldn't have allowed my good manners to be bullied by him. So, defiantly, I cracked a shell, popped a kernel in, and chewed the time I awaited his response.

All he did was stare at me. I felt the look searching my profile all through my cracking, shelling, and chewing three peanuts. I felt it score into my skin, seeking, assessing, deciding on my intent. I felt it make incorrect judgments about me, and find me close and stingy.

Recalling his fine, intelligent eyes, I pictured them now glazed with hurt and disappointment. I could almost feel his misery at my siege of the bag. So. What else to do? Again eye to bag, I took it up, removed a couple, and replaced it – that is, leaned over and pointedly spotted it quite near his leg. After all, I couldn't let the poor guy grovel.

The lightening-up of mood was marked. Tension whisked away. Graciousness mellowed the ambience as he accepted the hint and promptly lessened the bag once again, replacing it within his comfortable reach, and not too far out of mine. Then he relaxed completely into peanut consumption. By now though, distracted with curiosity, I just had to pass eyes over him.

First, it was his hands. So narrow and nimble, and swift at shelling and peeling, then flicking the peanuts into his mouth, so casual, so competent. Then it was his posture: relaxed to the point of a slouch; uncomposed, yet somehow natural and comfortable. Maybe it was the gray indistinctness of the evening that made his clothes seem ramshackle and too voluminous, shrinking him, and peculiarly explaining the boniness of those fine hands. But then I came to his face.

The sun had set off-shoulder behind him, leaving spot-bright that part of the early darkness, so some of his face remained mysterious in silhouette. Yet within that dimness were enough indications of my companion's features. A small, bearded, pointed face. Low brow. The striking eyes. The busily munching jaws. Instantly, though bewildering and ridiculous, an overall impression formed: the little guy did look uncannily like a larger monkey.

Once again my consternation sought refuge in the uniform grayness of the evening in front of me. Thinking through the blinking in my mind, I searched the darkness to see if I was being the victim of a practical joke. But the dusk remained sedately innocent. Which braved me to attempt a serious ascertaining look at my companion. For the monkey notion had left its doubtful lurk; it was poised to seize conviction as I breathed deeply and turned to find him just hopped off my bench and loping down the path.

I caught his single brief glance back, and was stunned by a queer thrill. For nothing more than smug was his look, and nothing less than amused. Those sharp monkey's eyes might've even been laughing at me. One certainly had winked.

Hooks

Zinovy Zinik

In America I would never run across people like him; they fly in circles too lofty for me to reach. As an *émigré*, I'd only encounter them in Europe, here in London or in Paris. But somehow I can never get used to them – it is either their casual familiarity, as if nothing untoward had occurred, or the reverse, the long, tragic face, as if you were attending your own funeral. That Moscow was, for me, irrecoverable was never discussed, as if the two of us just happened to be in London for a while and, whereas he had to get back shortly, certain urgent business compelled me to stay on. At least he didn't launch into the predictable discourse on the destiny of the West as seen through Russian eyes, the standard counterblast to *émigré* ideas on the destiny of Russia as seen through Western eyes. His own eyes were semi-transparent, dangerous-feeling, as though if you peered deeply into them myopia would set in and you'd never find your way out.

But he kept those eyes averted; he wasn't at ease either. He didn't know how to behave with me. I flattered myself that he might be feeling some shame in my presence. But perhaps I was merely assigning him noble feelings to put myself in a good light. Or it may have been an effect of the difference in our status: he was, after all, an industrial expert on an official exchange visit, the holder of a great state prize, the honored representative of Soviet history, whereas I, a wandering *émigré*, had been consigned by that same state to the blacklist with the dubious label of 'rootless cosmopolite.' Even that term belonged to his vocabulary, not mine – the vocabulary of the old wartime Stalinist generation. But, like most exiles, I was given to striking up acquaintance with strangers, and in hopes of being understood and accepted I would slavishly accommodate myself to their speech.

For someone like me, our meeting had the air of an ideological duel; he, on the other hand, must have found my agitation fascinating. He would keep his eyes averted; then suddenly, seemingly offhand, he would touch my shoulder lightly, or nudge my elbow, till I began to think that I had been wide of the mark in imagining any kind of official arrogance in his actions, or calculated condescension in his conversation.

Not that there was any real conversation. Actually, I couldn't understand why we were meeting at all. He had introduced himself as the uncle of my wife's high-school sweetheart back in Moscow. To that I found little to say; I thought of Yesenin's line: 'I am your nephew, you are all my uncles,' and Eichenvald's: 'All men are brothers; me, I'm a cousin.' But poetry was not one of his interests. On the other hand, he wasn't taking the occasion to make the usual Soviet visitor's request for either of the naked truths that Moscow banned: Solzhenitsyn's books or Soho's porn displays.

We were sitting in his seedy hotel room looking at one another with the simulated amicability of the dentist's waiting room. I couldn't make out why he said nothing – was it fear, plain indifference, or some inherent inability to start up a conversation? I repeated to myself my wife's admonitions on similar occasions: Don't worry about him, he's been in this situation before; he'll tell you what he wants soon enough. He was clearly not at all discomfited by the protracted pause, and like anyone accustomed to an iron curtain of silence he transferred to his companion the sense of guilt for the break in communication. It is in the nature of words to abhor silence; forgetting my wife's injunctions, I filled the air with overexcited and largely inconsequential talk:

'What really amazes me is my indifference. Actually, when I do feel drawn to Moscow it's the earlier Moscow I picture. What goes on there now, in fact, doesn't really interest me much. I mean, even the old notion that it's the people who stayed behind who betrayed *us*, and we *émigrés* are the heroes carrying on the battle without them – even that seductive old idea has lost its savor; those who betrayed us are no longer crucial to our happiness. If we get homesick, it's not for our actual home but the home of memory.'

'As to life in Moscow' – he finally resolved to interrupt my rambling meditations – 'I would quote from a poem I prize highly – Mezhirov: "The acts we put on may be sham, but you have to remember we're working without a safety net – one false step and we're smashed to smithereens."' I was silent. Well, of course. To hear them talk, their only concern is Absolute Truth, unlike the materialistic West, with its relativism and hypocrisy; prophetic fire, the endless task, all that. They might lie to each other, but it's always about great matters, for noble purposes; perhaps superficially, to the outsider's eye, things don't look right, but deep down inside it's all real and true. 'Smashed to smithereens' – the danger justifying the ends *and* the means. Yes indeed. I just hoped he wasn't going to start discoursing about 'inner freedom.' It seemed it was business as usual back there.

'The day they acknowledge what they did in the Hitler–Stalin Pact, that's the day I'll . . . ' I began, but I dried up. I recognised that look. My father, a Communist and a Jew, who lost a leg in the war, used to look at me that way when, in the heat of argument, I would blurt that if Hitler hadn't stirred up Russian patriotism Stalin and the whole Soviet system would have gone into the dustbin of history long ago. I wasn't afraid of my father's belt, much less his raised voice, but his tears made me feel terrible. It was with those same eyes, those pink-tinged lids, that the Muscovite visitor looked at me now. That was the worst thing, that defenseless look of a person who suddenly realises he is being viewed critically. I shouldn't have mentioned the war. That glance had betrayed a bitter nostalgia for those days. For him, the war must have been a unique period of freedom, when fate had granted his spirit the gift of a genuine patriotism; when it had been possible to defend the fatherland without orders from above or a pistol in the back of the neck: when he was issued a gun of his own and bullets to strike down what were enemies of the people in the true sense of the term, not in Stalin's. He might have been my own father – and I had absolutely nothing to say to him.

'Could you possibly help me find a certain little thing I want in London?' he asked in a pleading tone, and I sighed with relief. So – he, too, was after some piece of scarce merchandise; he was no exception after all. It just might have been conceivable that a man who'd worked his way up to responsible posts, titles, and decorations could remain a decent human even over there – well, it's nice to have one's skepticism validated, I said to myself. The old motherland can always come through with a fresh example of Darwinian principle – the evolution of the worthy idealistic Bolshevik model into an ape of material greed in response to his environment. Determinism shaping subspecies *Homo sovieticus* – an animal with a highly spiritual ideological mask over a primitive avaricious grimace. Yes, squirm as you like, you grow the way conditions ordain. It's pitiable, I suppose. But somehow my own spirit wasn't up to purging its revulsion.

'You couldn't take me to Oxford Street, could you?' asked the Soviet gent when I, despite my interior harangue, spoke aloud of my readiness to help.

'What part of Oxford Street?'

'Where the shops are.'

'It's all shops.'

'Fine, let's go there, then.' He added in a confidential whisper, 'I want some hooks.'

'Hooks? What sort of hooks?' I asked, somewhat flabbergasted.

'Fishing hooks,' he explained imperturbably and, rising slightly from his chair, poked two fingers into an inconspicuous watch pocket in his trousers; there was something tucked away in there, deep down, that refused to be brought to light. At last he withdrew a cellophane packet about the size of a matchbox. It, in turn, contained a piece of paper torn from a school exercise book and folded into four. I followed all these operations as if watching a conjurer at work. He proffered the folded note. On it enigmatic English words and names had been written with calligraphic exactitude; to the left of these was a no less puzzling column of figures with hieroglyphic curlicues – or were they drawings? It all looked like some spy cipher to me, and only served to intensify the false atmosphere of intimacy between us. Could he possibly have been sent by Moscow to recruit me into the KGB's Russian Literature Service, as we called it – to ask me to add my reports on London *émigré* activity to the files stacked inside the world's biggest humanities collection, the Lubyanka security headquarters? I looked up in alarm.

'It's a list. English fishing hooks with sizes. Can you give me a hand?' He moved his finger about the paper. Once again I began to flounder in that translucent gaze, trying to swim out of turbid water, keeping clear of whirlpools and shoals. They'd obviously gone off their heads over there, perched with their elite salaries beside the well-stocked ponds at their Politburo country dachas. Couldn't they manage with Soviet hooks? They must figure that even the cunning old pike of Russian folklore could never resist an elegant, unbreakable English hook. Maybe they heard of them in the handbook by Aksakov, our nineteenth-century Compleat Angler; for all his Slavophile outlook, he may have gone Anglophile himself when it came to recommending fishhooks.

'I can't go back to Moscow without hooks,' whimpered this man, this apparent adult. There it was again: Soviet civilisation turns everybody into a child where *things* are concerned; *things* are the toys of civilisation and the citizen of a vast country that hasn't many of them acts like a deprived child. You feel sorry for him, and irritated, and you know you can't shake him off. Ridiculing their puritanism as sham, though, is like calling a hungry man a hypocrite for taking a job advertising meat on a sandwich board. Like children everywhere, they simply must have material proof of their own idealism; thus Soviet people are materialistic idealists. Children have to be indulged, life won't give them a chance like this again – so we strode out the door in search of English fishhooks.

London was deluged in one of those spinning storms of rain and light you find only on this island, where the wind blows from four directions at once and you never know which way to turn to shield your eyes from the blinding droplets. We hung, as it were, in the timelessness of streaming rain, detached from the earth, pressed against one another, heads bent together like a pair of lovers: he'd left his umbrella in the hotel. We couldn't be bothered to go back for it, so the hurricane of rain and wind bore us along the side streets under one umbrella. The closer we became welded by the weather, the more alien I sensed his body to be, pressed against my shoulder in his smelly gabardine mackintosh and the sort of tartan cap that unversed tourists take to be typically English. He grated on me because of the absence of physical distance between us; I couldn't get free of him. To do that I would have to snag him with those special hooks, and we simply could not find any. These hooks turned out to be most rare and intricate, and the salesmen startlingly ignorant and rude. As we trudged for mile after mile along shopping streets, I subsided into a despairing resentment. I shook feverishly, either because of the penetrating wind or because of the intense exasperation I felt at the whole enterprise I'd been dragged into by that old business between my wife and the nephew of this Soviet fisherman.

One umbrella was clearly inadequate: my companion was

wearing a decent raincoat at least, whereas I had casually donned a corduroy jacket, which, as it absorbed the moisture, grew heavier and heavier, like an old soak under the Charing Cross arches. My back ached, my shoes squished, my throat was raw, and I cursed the Soviet regime for its false liberalism in letting perverts with English-fishhook fetishisms loose on London. We advanced in rushes, dashing through one glassy curtain of rain only to run into another, and as we halted to catch our breath in this jerky course we seemed to be on different landings of the same flight of stairs. No, it was as if two glass-cabined elevators had stopped for a second in a dark shaft and we gazed at one another through their walls: was it even conceivable we both lived under the same roof? Bound together, kin forever? That was all I needed of hell.

'Don't worry, I'm not trying to persuade you to go back,' said my Soviet gent. He didn't mean to the Old Country, he meant to Oxford Street, which we had left farther and farther behind – a mistake, in his view, since all shops that could possibly exist must be there. I could have no objection: I really didn't know where to go next. I'd got well off my planned route.

'I know what this rain reminds me of,' he said, wiping his face with a handkerchief as we were waiting out the next squall under an arch at Piccadilly Circus. 'This London rain reminds me of mosquito netting and the evening mist after a hot day at the dacha. It's just come back to me: your wife used to visit my nephew at the dacha. That was where I first saw her, maybe the last time, too. A slim schoolgirl she was, like a dandelion. They were walking together arm in arm, toward the terrace. Through a sort of haze like this rain. I was sitting with my sister on the terrace. Mist all round, you know, makes distances hard to judge. Mosquitoes and moths were flying around the lamp, and there was a sweet smell of paraffin. I remember that so well.'

He stopped as if hoping for an answering burst of lyricism. As it was, this nephew, whoever he might be, was getting on my nerves; 'Poor boy,' my companion would say whenever he mentioned my wife's adolescent admirer. I resolved to curtail these nostalgic evocations of dacha life at least.

'After three emigrations, from one country to another,' said I, 'my yearning for the Old Country long ago lost any geographical dimension. It's not connected physically with any one point on the earth's surface. My normal state of mind, generally speaking, is rather like the indisposition of middle age: it's a kind of equilibrium, when one agonising pain is balanced by another, newer one, which we know perfectly well we'll ignore as a third one looms up.'

'But where on earth is Eros?' he broke in, as if rebuking me for excessive intellectualism in my reflections. He was pointing, however, at the wooden hoarding in the center of the square. Black Eros – the winged messenger with his arrow of love, balanced on one foot on the top of the fountain in the center of Piccadilly Circus, that symbol of gay old London – was gone from behind the planking. I had to explain that Eros had been sent off for restoration. Eros was under repair, the fountain of the soul was dry, only intellect sparkled in neon signs through the shrouding rain. Britannia was poor and stingy; everyone was on his own.

'Won't I see Eros at all this time, then?' He shook a mournful head. Like all Soviet tourists, he further annoyed me with his rustic raptures over cliché London – the red buses, the black taxis, the bobbies in their crested helmets. I felt an imbecile urgency to maintain the reputation of my *émigré* life in those alien Russian eyes, as if to say, 'We have everything here, there's nothing you can't get. Especially rare and intricate fishhooks.' With a heavy sigh, I darted into the swirling rain.

It enveloped us in a dense, wavering veil, solidly separating off the rest of the world, which might have been anywhere: England, Russia, ancient Rome. I calculated that we were on Pall Mall, where that Jules Verne novel starts – what was it, 'Twenty Thousand Days Under the Sea' or 'Eighty Thousand Leagues Around the World'? The snowy-white columns of the club buildings gleamed through the bathysphere of rain as they loomed over us like Arctic icebergs, mist-enshrouded, and, as Captain Nemo might have done, I wanted to cry, 'To hell with this mercantile civilisation!' Retreating from the elements, we found ourselves in an arcade, where the window of another tackle shop floated before our eyes like the porthole of an aquarium. The salesman luring us inside could have been Captain Nemo himself, or a Russian bog monster. He seemed to be expecting us. He put on his tortoiseshell glasses and spent a long time chewing his lip over our crumpled list of magic figures and markings. Finally he informed us, with the solemnity of an oracle, that he did have these hooks but that 'they bend the other way.'

'That doesn't matter.' I hastened to explain this enigmatic phrase to my companion. 'It's like driving on the left – it's all relative. From the Russian viewpoint, they bend the way you want, you see what I mean?' By way of visual illustration, I absurdly twisted my head around nearly backward. I just wanted to make clear that the problem was resolved and I would go no farther. In the little shop it was dry, rather dark, and deserted as we sat down to wait at a table in the corner. There was something in that interior reminiscent of the Ark, pitching under the lashing assault of the storm. Around us were gleaming glass cases of mounted fish; nets and harpoons hung in the corners, fishing poles sprouted everywhere like exotic bamboo, and, most important, gigantic showcases held hooks of all sizes, shapes, and tints overlapping like metallic scales. My companion in his sodden raincoat reminded me of a shivering *dachnik*, stranded on a suburban station platform after missing the electric train.

And I remembered where I'd seen exactly the same suffering expression, reproach mixed with hope. Those same grimaces had been displayed by the old repairman in the typewriter shop on Kuznetskiy Most, when I brought my Olympia to him for the last time before I left the country. The very same heavy rain, Muscovite variety, had beset his premises, too, replete as it was with objects no less exotic than those in this tackle shop. How he'd fussed about, sighing and shaking his head, when he found out what far lands I was quitting Moscow for. How he'd started unscrewing the casing with excessive roughness to conceal his trembling fingers as they tugged out the accumulated dirt, hair, and assorted rubbish.

'You've got a cat at home, then,' he'd grumbled. 'I can tell what any household is like by the stuff in the typewriter.'

We had no cats at home – it was me going bald, not a cat – but never mind; he was just filling up a tense silence with his mutterings. Then he got out a jug of alcohol, but instead of using it to clean the keys he ran some tap water into it and banged down two glasses. I remember the light, acrid smell of the spirits and the mustiness of the basement shop, his tear-filled eyes and the network of blood vessels on his flaccid, alcoholic cheeks. And the dim gleam of the part in his brilliantined hair. An hour later, his hair sticking up wildly by now, he was recounting for the *n*th time his exploits as an air ace.

But finally he couldn't hold back, he burst the net of restraint: he had, he said, a Tatar friend – the carriage on the man's typewriter even went backwards, the Muslim way – but *he* had no plans to leave, even though Stalin had moved *him* to Siberia for a while. What was wrong with me, couldn't I sit still? He and the Tatar used to go fishing at a reservoir a mere hundred kilometres from Moscow, and he'd feel homesick even there; on the way back, the very mention of Moscow made his heart beat faster. How could anybody leave – forever? He just couldn't see that. He'd be glad to take me to that reservoir with a net, to get some big fish. Or in winter maybe, to sit out all night with a line through the ice. He'd found *yeriki* there, spots where the ice seals off the water and all the fish are caught inside as in a bucket: you could take them out with your bare hands.

I remember his oddly intent stare – and mine, shifty, though it should have been the other way round. I remember us sitting there for a long time, like now: close kin and at the same time totally alien. I couldn't argue with him, because the only ideas he could comprehend were foreign to me, and I can't convey alien thoughts in my own words.

*

The exotic word *yeriki* had taken me aback considerably – was it the resonance with 'eureka'? I even took the trouble to consult Dal's dictionary. I felt like that old gudgeon (or whatever inhabits Moscow reservoirs), gasping under the ice in those *yeriki*. Meanwhile outside, the yellow houses on Kuznetskiy Most were wet with rain. Yellow houses – Moscow isn't a fairy-tale snow-white city, it's a city of yellow houses. It was grim hauling my typewriter home past those sodden yellow façades; what sort of people was it who could construe your longing for peace of mind and for freedom as treachery? I remembered my fear, not of treason, or prison, but of becoming one of them myself, the fear of being defined, my fate ordained, by others. But how I longed to be back under the lowering Moscow skies at this moment; for any fear contains the hope of release from that fear, and the memory of that feeling of hope, which accompanied all the years I spent there, overcame the memory of fear. That insistent sense of a hope lost forever is in itself punishment for my decision to free myself permanently from fear. And lost along with that hope was the avidity of eye and finger, the pleasure, with which this stranger from my Soviet past was now picking over the shining fishhooks on the table. It was for the sake of this scene then – to witness another's appetite for my new life when I myself had grown blasé – that I had dragged along with this venerable Soviet official under an English cloudburst. It was for the joy of recognition in the eyes of the other – a perverse sense of nearness, no matter whether with friend or enemy. (No one is closer to being a sworn enemy than your best friend; the two can be almost the same.)

'You've saved a man's life, you should know,' said the Soviet fellow, looking up at me as if guessing my thoughts about him. 'You've saved a human being. Thank you.'

'No need to exaggerate,' I managed to bring out with affected nonchalance. 'You'd have survived somehow without English hooks.'

'Me? *I* would, of course. But what about my nephew?

Poor boy.' And his chin began to quiver. He reached for his handkerchief. The shopkeeper, off behind his counter, gazed through his tortoiseshell glasses at the vast window spattered with raindrops, pretending not to notice our corner mutterings in some incomprehensible and unreal tongue: for me, this heightened the sense of conspiracy, of the confessional, that surrounded the words of this elderly man, who had suddenly lost all traits of the Soviet. All that remained was his bewilderment at the perversity of fate and a mute plea for sympathy, nothing more. The mention of the nephew, again, annoyed me so much that at first I didn't take in what he was saying – about cards and billiards, about Dostoevsky's 'Gambler,' a woman, and underworld Moscow, and the odd idea of escaping from a politicised world into some sort of casino where stakes were high and payment was not in cash but in kind – and what an effort it had taken to get that list of English fishhooks out of prison. In jail they keep accounts their own way, he was saying: you don't pay up, your throat gets slit.

At length it began to dawn on me what my former countryman was talking about: these double-damned hooks were not destined for privileged bureaucrats to go catch sturgeon in Kremlin ponds, no. Lord knows *who* would be fishing with them, in what troubled waters. These hooks were the equivalent of beads for savages; they were treasury notes, legal tender, hard currency in the jailhouse banking system of incorrigible gamblers. The nephew was such a gambler, and he was in jail. 'If I hadn't looked you up in London, the poor boy . . . ,' and he made a gesture near his throat.

'You know,' he went on, 'I'd have washed my hands of that boy long since; he's a hopeless case.' My companion snorted into his handkerchief. 'But not long before he was arrested he took me to one of those awful restaurants I can't stand – people filling their faces, champing, belching, the orchestra hammering out some execrable stuff . . . I looked around at it all, and I quoted a line from I think it's Heinrich Heine: "To think the Redeemer died on the cross for these swine – what a waste!"

My nephew smiled a little, and said, "No, my dear uncle, your Heine was wrong. Decent folk can take care of their own salvation; it was precisely to save such miserable worms as these that the Fisherman got himself on the hook." Imagine! And I'd figured that good-for-nothing for a fool. How wrong can a man be?' He began stowing the English fishhooks about his person.

(*Translated, from the Russian, by Alan Myers.*)

The Deal

Pierre Tran

The walls and carpets of the New York office are a soft grey and the halogen uplights on slim black stands in the corners of the room give discreet backwashes of light. Forsythe, dressed in his lightweight two-piece grey mohair suit, sits at his solid ashwood desk. He has hung Turner reproductions to add to the understated look he has imported to this prime high-rise real estate. Soft-spoken product of an English school founded in the seventeenth-century and a blue-blooded merchant bank he is equally dislocated.

There are three of them facing him across the Desk. Rawlings of Rawlings Leisure Industries, there to discuss a highly speculative East European venture, his vice-president Larry Haskins and the inevitable lawyer.

'Hey you are so lucky to have these beautiful offices,' Haskins opens the conversation, softening Forsythe for the pitch.

Forsythe stares at him levelly. 'What's luck got to do with it?'

Haskins glances across to Rawlings, who immediately picks up the lead, 'OK, so what is the deal here . . . Everyone is telling me the new markets are in Eastern Europe. You know the first thing the newspapers and magazines did when censorship came off over there? They went across to the West, bought suitcase-loads of adult publications and remade them with their own cut and paste job.'

Rawlings is a pornographer, publishing what he calls adult literature and worth millions. He is looking for fresh business opportunities as his home market is saturated. Rawlings Leisure Industries is being squeezed by the clean-up lobby and the hard-core producers who take a bigger share of the market each year.

Rawlings has done his homework. 'Those East European countries have been producing Warsaw-Pact-standard weapons for years. They have warehouses full of automatic rifles, spare parts and ammunition.'

He pauses, exchanging unspoken communication with Haskins before moving in for the kill. The deal he proposes involves his porn magazines in exchange for Kalashnikov semi-automatic rifles. The guns to be shipped to the States, where Rawlings plans to wholesale them. The East Europeans get to keep the local currency revenues from the magazine sales, plus a percentage of the dollar sales to meet their hunger for hard currency.

Rawlings leans back expansively as he ends the sales pitch: 'The one thing your average red-blooded American male likes to do at home or on vacation is show off his self-defence armament or sporting rifle.'

Forsythe listens impassively, his manicured hands clasped in front of him. 'You are talking about a barter trade deal relating to adult publications and foreign arms.' The query, like everything he does, is framed with care. 'What are the regulatory constraints?'

The lawyer confidently steps in. 'We have looked at the regulatory approvals. This will be a legitimate sporting goods transaction conducted through a Delaware-incorporated subsidiary of Rawlings Leisure Industries. It's separately capitalised and held at arm's length. The items will be converted to single-shot capability by a reputable manufacturer, stored in a bonded warehouse and shipped only to licensed gun dealers.'

Rawlings leans forward with a big smile. 'We will undercut every other supplier of long guns with this deal, and *I* get to unload my inventory. *You*, Forsythe, get a top slice of the pre-tax profit in return for your injection of risk capital.'

He already knows the details. Rawlings needs his European business contacts, to sign up delivery contracts with the arms factories and get the necessary ministry approvals and permits. Forsythe shakes hands with Rawlings and nods to Haskins and the lawyer when the meeting comes to an end. He shows no feeling as they file out of the room.

After they have gone he reflects on the deal that is set to make him millions – perhaps many times over. Guns for porn. It's simple, it's elemental. A deal that sells itself. The one every corporate finance textbook tells you to look for. You could write it on the back of an envelope, and Rawlings brought it to him! Forsythe, of all people.

He hears the passing siren of a police car waw-wawing its way through the grimy Manhattan street outside in the real world. Is it yet another shooting incident? Perhaps a domestic row ended with a Saturday Night Special, or a crack dealer's Uzi sub-machine-gun. Soon the market will be flooded with cheap AK47s courtesy of Forsythe and his new business associates.

Down below, dirty rain splashes the sidewalks as the office workers hurry for the subway and bag people hunker down in doorways. Headlights reflect on the shiny black wet streets and drivers blare their horns as traffic grinds to a standstill. Forsythe stands looking through the black glass window. 'Not my problem,' he mutters to himself.

The raindrops glitter under the hard tungsten and neon lights, falling into the gutters choked with garbage. The rain does not wash away the filth of the streets but adds to the decay process with its wetness. Over on the East River grey rain falls on grey water carrying the black night soil of the city into the sea. 'Just a few more guns,' he murmurs.

He is protected, cocooned from the cold and wet, his black skyscraper a powerful barrier of commerce and wealth. A solitary crow flies past as he stands looking down. Forsythe no longer sees the city. His thoughts take him back to boyhood, young face upturned to a different scene.

A high wind tosses a crow across a leaden sky the colour of black rags dragged through water that's washed the floor. Grey heaviness descends from solid billowing clouds. Underneath, the earth lies drained of all colour and light. Even the grass seems to have lost its greenness as it moves like the pelt of a sleeping animal under the uneasy air.

Where does the crow fly on a day like this when the elements conspire to keep all living things under cover? Solitary creature, carrion eater, bird of ill omen. He sees that solid, distinctive blackness in its solitude, half flying, half borne by the turbulence, in the midst of the greyness of the world.

Lost in the gathering darkness he remembers the celebration barbecue thrown by Ted Marshall a year ago to mark the closure of the deal they had made. A barbecue by the poolside of a sprawling beach house: *how quaint*. In London it would have been a signing ceremony followed by drinks in the boardroom with crystal glasses and rare roast beef to follow.

A late September sun warms the evening. Marshall presides over a gas-fired range on the patio while a small knot of casually but expensively dressed people stands holding long drinks. 'Hey Forsythe! Get your ass over here and grab yourself a drink.' He gestures over the huge slabs of steak and burgers: 'What will it be – debt or equity?'

A tall slim woman coolly draped in white detaches herself from the group and greets Forsythe with a warm, open smile. 'I'm so glad you could make it over.' She takes his arm and steers him away from the other guests. 'I'm Lisa, Ted's my lucky husband.'

He had hesitantly accepted the surprise invitation after the business meeting had closed with Marshall.

She turns her blue-grey eyes on him. 'So you're Forsythe,

the great deal-maker that everyone's talking about. Ted called me from the office right after he signed off on the deal. He's on a high, calls it the deal of the decade.'

Forsythe, trying to work out the colour of her eyes, realises her hair almost glows, somewhere between fair and auburn in the soft evening light. Was it a trick of the fading sun? 'Really, you're too kind, I only played a small part in the financing,' he says. 'Your husband is a very shrewd businessman who can spot value in the market – I'm just an adviser.'

Her hair falls to her shoulders, making her look younger than the forty or so years he gives her. Her full lips grace her face with a look of friendliness but the warmth of her smile is tinged with knowing. 'They all say what a perfectly charming man you are, not forever talking about your top ten deals like all the others who work for Ted. I wonder,' she says thoughtfully, 'where manners end and pretending begins. You look like a nice man, Mr Forsythe, but I'm sure you're tough inside, maybe even cruel – I wonder what it would take for the inside to come out, how long before the act slips?'

'So what do *you* do, Mrs Marshall?' Forsythe does what he normally does when he runs for cover: he asks a question back.

'It's Lisa, OK. I'm studying for my Master's in English. I'm exploring the concept of "negative space" in Conrad's novels.'

This is too much for his thin pragmatic English blood. He has secured financing for a big US deal, is weekending on Long Island instead of flying home to Virginia Waters. Standing next to a beautiful stranger he has just been psychoanalysed and is now talking about something called negative space. He cuts her off in mid-sentence as she talks about her thesis: 'Excuse me, er, Lisa, but could you tell me why I'm here?'

'Well, it was my idea to get you out here. Ted called from his office, said what a great guy you were, that the deal was all down to you, so I wanted to meet you.' She takes his arm again, gently pulling him to her side. He feels her softness against his arm as she starts to walk. Her head inclines: 'Ted trusts you – I want you to hear him out on a business offer.'

*

'I like you, Forsythe. You do good work, but you like to work alone, right? You've done some good deals, made fat fees for your house. Everyone's saying what a nice guy you are, so how come you aren't on the inside track to the main board?'

Forsythe is sitting with Marshall in his den. Impassive. He listens hard, because he knows listening is a survival skill.

'The thing is,' Marshall continues, 'your pals back home love the choice-looking deals you serve up, but fact is you're a loner and they don't trust loners. You don't drink with the boys that matter so they will shaft you royally when it comes to handing out directorships and top-line packages. Look, shit like that happens all the time – but you Brits have refined it to an art.'

'Excuse me Ted, I'm not sure I follow you.'

'Don't get me wrong, Forsythe. Back home you're on a dead end run but over here . . . well, over here I'm willing to set you up. My capital and your know-how. You spot the deals, and we'll roll the dice together.'

Forsythe is appalled by Marshall's vulgarity, fascinated by his crude simplicity. He thinks of his mock-Georgian house in England, Saturday bridge nights, the lawnmower that needs mending and Mary – kind sensible Mary. Through the open french windows he sees that the swimming pool lights have been switched on in the dusk: how they sparkle on the water. He thinks of Lisa and her discourse on *Nostromo* before he had interrupted her.

Now he stands by his Manhattan office window and wonders if he will call Marshall to sell this latest deal. He picks up the phone and dials.

'It's almost midnight!' the familiar voice protests. 'What on earth are you doing calling at this hour of the night?'

'I'm sorry, Mary, I just thought it's been a long time.' He talks about the deal and when he finishes she surprises him with her next question.

'Why are you over there, Christopher?'

'What do you mean, "why"? It's the job.'

'But you made plenty of money here. Instead you left me, your friends, everything for a job you hate. I know you hate it even though you never come out and say it. Why don't you come home?'

'Home to what? I never belonged. I was always acting, always pretending, but the funny thing was, it didn't work.'

'You don't have to pretend, Christopher. Everyone likes you, everyone thinks you're a sweet man.'

'You don't understand, do you! I've been pretending all my life. I went to a school where you were expected to conform, to believe in certain things. I went along with it even though I could see through it, hated it. I wanted to belong.'

'But that's a long time ago.'

'It never stops. They expect you to act certain ways and you go along with it to be polite. Somewhere along the way pretending becomes more real than your own feelings. It's like watching someone else's life, Mary.'

'So you went to New York to be free? But all you did was find a new part to act. The horrid Englishman who eats merchant bankers isn't you either, Christopher. You don't belong there.'

'I don't belong in England either. I wouldn't have thought twice about rejecting this deal back in London, but here everything is possible. This deal will show all those hypocrites at home just what deal-making is all about.'

'Please, Christopher, it's a sordid little deal and you know it, otherwise you wouldn't be calling me in the middle of the night to justify it to me.'

'The beauty is that it *is* so horrible. I want to do it to show those mediocrities what I can do. I'll have the money and they'll be sick with envy, but won't dare to admit it, "Poor Forsythe," they'll say, "lost his sense of decency." '

'If you would only listen to yourself! This is children's talk in the playground. There's more to life than paying back old scores. Think of the consequences. These are real guns, they can kill. You have to live with yourself.'

'I'm just putting the deal together, it's not my finger on the trigger.'

'You don't really want to do it.'

He feels the tears sting his eyes – realises the act of crying actually hurts as he weeps for the loss of his ability to feel. There is only emptiness left behind.

'Poor Christopher, I hope you find what you want – I hope it's worth it.'

Forsythe bids his ex-wife goodnight and hangs up. Now he knows what negative space is. The holy doctors of the Church no longer say Hell is everlasting fire but a permanent sense of loss, a separation from goodness. In the secular canyons of Wall Street Forsythe feels a separation from himself. A loss of his own nature.

Then he remembers a fragrance of peach blossom, of wholesomeness on an Indian summer evening. He suffers a pang of longing for an unattainable beauty. What colour was her hair, her eyes? She will never be his, could never be his, so he no longer cares. It seems to him his choice has already been made. Already he has broken with the past, now he will break with the hope of a future.

Forsythe decides to remake himself in the only way he knows how. 'I love this deal!' he says to himself. He dictates a message to his assistant to pull the East European files first thing in the morning and then extinguishes the halogen uplights. He stops on his way out of the darkened room, returns to his desk and adds another instruction into his dictating machine.

'Please be so kind as to arrange for the watercolours to be taken down in the next few days. Leave the walls bare. Thank you.'

He may decide to replace them with something else; he may not.

A Repertoire

Michael Donoghy

'Play us one we've never heard before'
we'd ask this old guy in our neighborhood.
He'd rosin up a good three or four
seconds, stalling, but he always could.
This was the Bronx in 1971,
when every night the sky was pink with arson.
He ran a bar beneath the el, the Blarney Stone,
and there one Easter day he sat us down
and made us tape as much as he could play;
'I gave you these. Make sure you put that down',
meaning all he didn't have to say.

All that summer we slept on fire escapes,
or tried to sleep, while sirens or the brass
from our neighbour's Tito Puente tapes
kept us up and made us late for mass.
I found our back door bent back to admit
beneath the thick sweet reek of grass
a nest of needles, bottlecaps, and shit.
By August Tom had sold the Blarney Stone
to Puerto Ricans, paid his debts in cash
but left enough to fly his body home.

The bar still rises from the South Bronx ash,
its yellow neon buzzing in the noonday
dark beneath the el, a sheet-steel door
bolted where he played each second Sunday.
'Play me one I've heard before'
I'd say, and whether he recalled those notes
or made them up, or – since it was Tom who played –
whether it was something in his blood
(cancer, and he was childless and afraid)
I couldn't tell you. And he always would.

Transport

Fred D'Aguiar

The cobbled streets shone
with rain or sleet or snow.
We drove leaving these
oblique tracks on water,
consumed by light or frost
that was light's colour.

All this through a heated
rear window in a bus I'd
boarded or had been made
to board with faces
lumped together strictly
on the basis of race.

Why was I at the rear
looking out at weather
I couldn't even define?
Perhaps it was dawn.
Perhaps? Of course! Streetlights
made the streets shine.

I wore pyjamas,
a bathrobe and was barefoot.
No time to grab my glasses.
I saw the world more as
conjecture than fact.
That at least's a fact!

I knew no one on that bus.
Talk was forbidden,
by whom I don't know.
I heard the engine rev
as it climbed and descended
through several gears.

I felt cobbles or potholes
on a rear axle I feared
might break: an old bus
or a bad road, or both;
tires parting the wet road,
and the parts closing behind.

It's weather I don't like
to be out in, much less
barefoot wearing bed things.
Heading where? East
I guessed from the sky,
or what I took for sky –

a whitish gray light
opening like a huge parasol
at the front of the bus,
and the bus continually
heading into it as it
gracefully retreated,

or could not be caught
beyond the fringe that laced
the bonnet, windscreen,
wing mirrors and front
hub caps, acting like a
magnet on that bus and us.

Why did I think just then
we were all going to die
or had already died
and the lights were God's –
his chariot, his humble
bearing chariot

spiriting homeward all
who had perished that night
in the black district.
The thought wasn't just mine.
Everyone looked like they
saw what was in my mind,

as if my skull was shaved away
showing my brain in its brine.
The cobbled stones that shone
were clouds we sailed above.
The engine noise I heard
was my own breath and heart.

Walking Across the Brooklyn Bridge, July 1990

Sujata Bhatt

In New York
children are being shot
to death this summer.
It's usually an accident.
Someone else, no doubt an adult,
was meant to be killed instead.
It's not a war,
just a way to settle disagreements.

Walking across the Brooklyn Bridge
one feels removed from everything
as if one were passing by
                    in a low flying plane.
Below, on both sides the cars
stream by. Above, the steel
cables converge, tighten.
The muscles in my legs feel
exposed, worn out.

The children somehow get in
the way: They're found dead
in the car, in the house,

in the crib. Sometimes it happens
that the father
was cleaning the gun.

Walking across the Brooklyn Bridge
today I see work being done.
Repairs. Clean, clear-cut
adjustments. Renovation.
The humming of steel against wind
drills through my bones –
it's driven up my spine.
The humming does not end.

But the worst case
I read about didn't involve a gun.
Simply a father, newly arrived from Montana
who decided to feed
his six-day-old son
to a hungry German Shepherd.
Was the mother really asleep?

Walking across the Brooklyn Bridge
I pause, look around.
What is real in this symbol,
in that other one over there . . . ?
The steel cables have become a cage,
a sanctuary. Whose cage?
Whose hope?

In another section
of the newspaper I read
about the ever growing problems of refugees.
Who will take them in?
Especially the ones from Vietnam,
a favourite subject for photographers:
flimsy boats, someone's thin arm in the way –

Who can forget those eyes?
And who can judge those eyes
                    that vision?

   Walking across the Brooklyn Bridge
   even on a hot afternoon
   one sees many joggers.
   And there is the view, of course.

Looking across the water
I think of those people from Vietnam.
The mothers, the fathers,
what they wouldn't have given,
what they would still give –
their blood, their hair, their livers, their kidneys,
their lungs, their fingers, their thumbs –
to get their children
past the Statue of Liberty.

Coma

Mimi Khalvati

Mr Khalvati? Larger than life he was;
too large to die so they wired him up on a bed.
Small as a soul he is on the mountain ledge.

Lids gone thin as a babe's. If it's mist he sees
it's no mist he knows by name. *Can you hear me,*
Mr Khalvati? Larger than life he was

and the death he dies large as the hands that once
drowned mine and the salt of his laugh in the wave.
Small as a soul he is on the mountain ledge.

Can you squeeze my hand? (Ach! Where are the hands
I held so tight to pull me back to the baize?)
Mr Khalvati? Larger than life he was

with these outstretched hands that squeezing squeeze
thin air. Wired he is, tired he is and there,
small as a soul he is on the mountain ledge.

No nudging him out of the nest. No one to help him
fall or fly, there's no coming back to the baize.
Mr Khalvati? Larger than life he was.
Small as a soul he is on the mountain ledge.

A Gujarati Patient Speaks

Sujata Bhatt

*A heart surgeon in London made it a practice to operate only after he and his patient had both listened to Gould recordings.**

Usually, when I'm sick
I eat rice with yoghurt,
two cloves of raw garlic
and some દાળનું પાણી (dalnu pani).

After the dal has settled
on the bottom of the pot
I scoop out the top-water,
rich with onions and garlic –
I squeeze fresh lemon juice
over it in my bowl
drink it slowly –
Usually, I feel much better.

Coriander is important.
And fenugreek.
I use lots of fenugreek.

* The above quotation is from *Glenn Gould: A Life and Variations* by Otto Friedrich, Lester & Orpen Dennys Ltd, Toronto, 1989

Although I live in London
I still prefer my ways.
Sitar, tabla: I call them my basic
instruments because they help me
improve my mood, soothe my headaches.

When I hear certain notes
I can smell patchouli,
I can smell my mother's soap
and the oil she used on her hair.

So when my doctor asked me
to listen to all this Bach,
The Goldberg Variations –
I thought he must know
something about Ayurvedic methods.

But why Bach?
And why Glenn Gould?
Normally, I don't listen to piano.
Even my children prefer saxophone –
  and mostly jazz.

Still, this morning after breakfast
I gave it a try.
Glenn Gould: such movement, exact
the way honeybees measure
  and remeasure the sun
all summer – pink zinnias –
urgent wings hum after
the shifting angle of earth and sun.

And if there is sleep in the background
it is the sleep of a man
with too many dreams –
and it is the sleep of lovers
who can't ignore each other.

I can see why a surgeon
would worship the gestures,
lust after the fingers behind this sound.

But me? How will the piano
understand my moods?

Growth

Adam Lively

– Inside this fat person, there's a thin person trying to get out.

– Just the one, dear?

I was thin once, though you wouldn't think it to look at me. I've got crevices in my crevices. The change happened when I was aboard Pan Am flight 003 from Heathrow to Kennedy Airport, New York. Not immediately, of course – I didn't gorge myself on shrink-wrapped chicken salad, stuff myself silly with plastic cheese and tiny tomatoes. It was more a change in my state of mind, a mental dislocation that meant that I stopped being a thin person and became, in embryo, something bigger. And sadder. And wiser.

I arrived at the university where I was to do my post-graduate studies in the early hours of the morning, and on the wrong day. No one was expecting me. I remember sitting forlornly beside my suitcases, being stared at by the Dean of Faculty's teenage daughter while her mother made arrangements, and already I felt the change coming over me. I think it was something to do with the air, because later, when I was chomping through sloppy joes and hamburgers, it felt like I needed extra ballast. If I didn't take on board all that extra stuff, I might simply float away.

My room was above the college kitchens, so hours in advance I could smell what was going to be on offer and plan my menu accordingly. There were only two other rooms on my floor, both occupied by female undergraduates. We shared an open-plan bathroom where steam from the shower unit mixed with the smell of the toilet to form a permanent, smelly fug. I was quite attracted to one of these undergraduates – she was called Susan and was 'just crazy about anything to do with England' – but of course nothing came of it. It's hard to spark a romance when you know so much about each other's insides.

Meals became the anchorpoints of my life. They were organised on a serve-yourself, eat-as-much-as-you-like system. I did. My flesh began to express itself in other ways too. Before I went to America I'd hardly ever been ill – just a bout of glandular fever and a broken wrist. But now things began to happen to my body in a way that made it feel like it had taken on a life of its own and whatever it was of me that wasn't my body was a powerless bystander. In the past I'd had occasional fits of absent-mindedness, anguished weeks when I'd lose my glasses, my wallet, my scarf, even my shoes. My possessions would trickle through my fingers like water. What I was going through now was a similar kind of forgetfulness, only what I'd lost this time – maybe it was rolling about on the floor of Flight 003 – was some vital connection between myself and my own flesh.

The first thing that happened was that I developed a large sebaceous cyst ('a swelling of the skin due to blockage of the duct of a sebaceous gland and distension with sebaceous secretion') behind my left ear. Like most teenagers, I'd waged long and bitter campaigns against acne, and thought I'd perfected the technique for dealing with it: wait for the optimum moment (timing is the key) then with a squeeze and a satisfying squirt against the bathroom mirror, the problem is solved. But this thing behind my ear was more intractable – or perhaps I'd lost the single-minded patience of youth. The more I pinched and squeezed it, the more inflamed and virulent it became. The skin on the surface became hard and scaled, while behind it a balloon-like sack of 'sebaceous secretion' accumulated. Pus, to you or me.

I began to find it hard meeting people. The university collected Englishmen like first editions, and I was always being asked to attend functions. But I was becoming more and more self-conscious about the red balloon that was causing my left ear to bulge out. When I was talking to someone, I took to presenting them with my right profile, but I think this made me seem rather aloof, as though I were always looking over the other person's shoulder for someone else more interesting to talk to. To add to my air of hauteur, I had also gone slightly deaf, though I later discovered that this was due not to my cyst but to an unrelated infection of the middle ear.

My only friend was an Oregonian called Greg. We shared a passion for country-and-western music, while he also had passions (which I didn't share) for medieval romances and Jacques Derrida. He always seemed to be reading either *Gawain and the Green Knight* or *Of Grammatology*. When it came to my sebaceous cyst, Greg tried to console me with the thought that things could be a whole lot worse – the composer Scriabin had actually died of a zit. Apparently, he had been working on a huge, mystical piece of music that would be so mind-blowing that when it was premiered, at the top of a mountain in the Himalayas, the entire universe would dissolve. ('Scriabin was a pretty interesting kind of a guy,' Greg commented.) Unfortunately (or fortunately, depending on your point of view) before he could finish it he developed a zit underneath his moustache and died from blood poisoning. It was a good story, and that must have been a hell of a zit. But it didn't cheer me up much.

It was about that time, when I was beginning to get fatter and my sebaceous cyst was ripening nicely, that I fell in love with Molly Whalen. Actually it was more of an infatuation, and a lot of it was because I was egged on so much by Greg. I think he looked on me as a character from one of his romances, an exotic and amusing Don Quixote figure who'd galloped over from the Old World to the New in order to tilt at windmills. It fitted his image of me perfectly that I should fall hopelessly in love with a beautiful and already attached undergraduate. Molly Whalen, who was Canadian, had a dancer's body, a moon face, and skin of such perfect, translucent whiteness that beneath each eye it was delicately tinged with blue. Even now that detail brings a lump to my throat. Greg encouraged me to compose country-and-western songs on the subject of my unhappiness ('Molly Whalen's got me howlin' like a loon/ Molly Whalen's got me wailin' at the moon'), and when I told him about those heart-stopping glimpses of blueness beneath her cheeks he told me that I should compose a book-length ode in praise of that one feature of my beloved. It was what the troubadours would have done. What with the poetry, the overeating, my cyst and Molly Whalen, things were getting too much for me. I was beginning to weep a lot.

Then came the injury to my finger. I was coming through the heavy glass swing doors in the basement of the library one day, when I saw Molly coming the other way. As usual, I felt like my guts had fallen to the bottom of my shoes. I grinned ingratiatingly at her, and as someone passed her and came through the other door I put my fingers around the glass of my door to hold it open. We had a date to go to a film that night – my first date with her – and I wanted to remind her in case she'd forgotten. What I didn't notice was that the other door was swinging back, and as I stood there, staring inanely at Molly, it fell back and crushed the middle finger of my left hand. The strange thing was that I didn't even notice. Molly Whalen was like an anaesthetic. It was only when I was standing in front of her, gabbling excitedly, that I noticed that she was staring downwards and that she was looking whiter than usual. I looked down too. There were streaks of blood on my trousers, and a pool of it accumulating on the marble floor.

She took me across the campus to the hospital. My finger was wrapped in her handkerchief. I was in heaven. For a moment I really did feel like a wounded knight being tended by his lady.

(Though Greg, who was reading Freud by this time, said that maybe the whole thing was an expression of my repressed fear of – and desire for – castration at the hands of Molly Whalen.) The doctors operated to remove what was left of my nail, strapped up my arm in a sling and dosed me up with painkillers. Molly was waiting for me, and we went to the movies together that night as planned. It was the greatest night of my life. The film was *Rear Window*, and I identified totally with James Stewart in his wheelchair. I was sky-high on the painkillers. Every few minutes Molly would move close to me and breathe in my ear, 'You OK?' and I would sigh back, 'Fine. Just fine.'

Molly was willing to offer me sympathy for my crushed finger and sebaceous cyst, but nothing more. As the moon of my courtship waned, my cyst flared up. The doctor decided to lance and drain it. (His language was horribly graphic.) I remember that when he was performing the operation, under local anaesthetic, the nurse in attendance, rather unprofessionally, gasped 'Yuk, that is *gross.*' And that wasn't the end of the pain and humiliation visited on me by my cyst. Every morning for three weeks afterwards I had to change the dressing myself, a delicate and excruciating operation involving lengths of gauze tape and a pair of tweezers, and all performed in my smelly bathroom under the prurient eye of my neighbour Susan. Greg suggested I should ask Molly to help me with it, but I didn't think that was such a good idea.

And so it went on. Life seemed to dribble out of me like the sebaceous secretions from my sebaceous cyst. Summer came and Molly, who I now saw only at a distance, seemed to have acquired an extra radiance. I ate vats of spaghetti carbonara. I joined the university's cricket team and got knocked out when I failed to get out of the way of the ball in time. The doctor – the same one who'd operated on my finger – thought it was pretty funny that an English guy should come all the way to America to be concussed by a cricket ball. I ate.

I never finished my postgraduate degree. America had defeated me. A week after I had fled back to London, I met up with an old girlfriend. When Karen and I were squeezed into the snug of a pub in Holloway, I asked her tentatively if she thought America had changed me.

'Put it like this,' she said. 'It's lucky you didn't become a cowboy, because you'd never get your finger in the trigger.'

The Gathering

Joan Riley

Adella shifted restlessly in her chair, half-listening to the increasing volume of conversation as it flowed around her. She wished she could walk away from the noise and constant activity as Carol refilled a glass here, or brought some more food over there. The overhead light hurt her eyes, taking away comfort and gloom from the tiny room, revealing it cluttered to overflowing with plates, glasses and the untidy litter of bodies.

'Is like dem keep Binkie fa me an a doan even dead yet,' she thought resentfully, wishing she was still at work and could join in with the gossip and the amusement. Not that she wasn't interested; she loved to hear about the goings on around the street, what people at work were up to, even the price of yam in the market. But Lisa always told her those things, repeating them with a humour that was hard to match.

It was not that she did not like company, but right now she was missing John Wayne on the television. She had planned her whole Saturday to leave space for him. Now the room was overflowing with people all coming to see how she was; and her head ached with the laughter and the constant loud talk. Trust them to all come on Saturday evening.

'Why black people always haffe tink same tought,' she wondered morosely, watching Mr Peters tear into his fourth piece of fried chicken. She felt a nudge at her elbow, turned to see Carol bending over her, face full of annoyance.

'We're running out of food again, Mum, and Lisa say her back's hurting and she's hungry.'

Adella sighed. What did they expect her to do about it? She felt a sudden anger at Mr Peters. That man never visited her from one day to the next, even though he only lived two doors down the street and had rented from her when she still had a house. Yet let food and noise seep out of her door and he would be there dressed nice and neat like a Sunday afternoon visitor.

'So why yu no stop give Missa Peters all de food? Yu no see ow ihm a shovel it weh?'

Carol looked shocked. 'You know I can't do that, Mum,' she said pleadingly.

'Een eh?' Adella responded absently, adding, 'A doan know ow de man can eat like dat. Fram a know Missa Peters, ihm have false teeth, an ihm still manage tough, tough meat that even me caan eat.'

'Dat's cause he use something to fix them on.'

Adella snorted. 'So ow come las year when ihm go a Delroy wedding ihm teeth fall out in de rice an peas, mek people see ow ihm mouth mash?'

She wasn't really interested in an answer, and Carol straightened and moved away after giving her a last reproachful look.

Adella wished Lisa would stop cooking and come and keep her company, talk to her and make her laugh. Trust Lisa to come to her house and take charge. She had done that for so long, it seemed like second nature. But they left her all alone marooned in her chair, cut off from the conversation, the company. It was her room, yet now it was strange and alien – full of noise, harsh barks of laughter, raised voices, bodies packed and wedged untidily together. It was too small a room to entertain a lot of guests.

She knew she should make an effort, especially during the lulls in the conversation. That was when they would turn to her.

Miss Matty, all dressed up in new hat and Sunday shoes, her daughter beside her, mouth still open after fifteen years of marriage, as if she caught the flies her mother was so scared of. You could count on Miss Matty to come visiting on Saturday afternoon and tell everybody else besides. She could imagine the woman in the market, probing and feeling the ground provisions with withered hands. Rejecting a pear because it wasn't fit, a piece of pumpkin because it was force ripe. All the time her darting eyes moving from side to side in case she missed some gossip. Each small event packed in with her shopping, stored carefully and dusted off when she descended like John Crow on the victim of her weekly visit. Rumour had it that Matty was so thin because she dared not keep still, in case a piece of scandal pass her by. Adella felt sorry for the woman's daughter. How old was she now? Twenty-seven and still in her mother's shadow, still dragged around from place to place though she had children of her own and a man to look after.

Her eyes shifted to Mr Peters's fat cheeks bulging with a load of food, lips beaded with grease like colourless lipstick. His eyes never left his plate as if he feared someone would snatch something if he glanced away. He talked endlessly, words muffled through the load inside his mouth. Food and conversation, that was all Mr Peters needed. Since his wife died and his children moved away he had grown steadily fatter, eating out on old war stories and things that happened when he came to England.

The harsh sound of the doorbell cut through the smoke and noise inside the room. Adella shrank further into her chair, wondering where anyone else could fit. They were all around her, spilling over into the dining-room, crammed together in noisy disarray. She heard the hurtling, yelping sound of Shela running to crash against the door, voices raised but indistinct. When a head popped round the door she relaxed.

She had forgotten Audrey was coming round, that she had made another appointment for her to see a special doctor. She wished Audrey would come inside, sit down and talk to her instead of taking a quick look around and retreating in haste. She knew where she was going, into the kitchen with Carol and Lisa. They were having a good time in there and she felt almost resentful when she heard their cheerful laughter mingling with the clamour all around her.

Adella's head felt heavy and she wished her visitors would go. She wanted to open the window and allow the stuffiness to drift away with them. Her mind drifted to her daughters. 'A wonda when de next docta visit is?' she thought suddenly. She hated going to see the doctor, had seen too many recently, yet still her daughters insisted.

'Mum, there has to be something wrong,' they often said. 'You're just not yourself.'

'Ole age, man,' she tried to tell them, but all they did was shake their heads and make another appointment. She remembered the disaster of the last one.

It was Audrey who had taken her, coming round in the nice blue car, making her swell with pride as she guided her down the outside steps. Adella had been glad of the pains in her foot that forced them to walk so slowly. Her heart had lifted as she saw curtains twitching and Mr Peters passing. 'Is me daughter, man, she come fa me in her car,' she had told him unnecessarily, since he had known Audrey since she was a child. It was nice to boast a little, especially since it gave her the excuse she needed to raise her voice so that the hidden watchers behind twitching net curtains could hear her.

'Dem too fast in dem one anada business,' she replied unrepentantly when her daughter complained: 'De way dem stay yu caan do one ting on dis street widout de whole world know it.'

Audrey had looked at her with raised brows, but her mother had ignored it, allowing her to help her into the car and fit the belt into its slot. Audrey didn't understand. It was different when Adella stood for hours peering out of her curtains. She had to know what was going on, keep an eye on things and such like. Anyway, she was trapped inside most of the time and before, when she had been at work – well she *had* to look out to see what was going on. How else could she talk about it? It would never do to have somebody telling her what was happening on her street, and she not knowing enough to join the conversation.

The journey to the doctor always took a long time. There were so many people she knew, especially on Loughborough Road. It was almost empty of houses now, full of the sprawling tangled yellow brick of Stockwell Park estate. She had Audrey stop for many acquaintances, make sure they had a good look at the car. 'Is me daughter,' she would say proudly, even though they knew, but needing to voice her pride somehow. 'She did go a university and now she have big jab wid de council.' The woman or man would make a few comments and she would always have to draw their attention to the car. 'Yu like de car?' she would ask casually. 'Is she did buy it, you know. Fram she learn to drive.' Other people she would wave to, getting Audrey to blow the car horn, feeling important as they looked up, startled. By the time she finished she knew that the whole neighbourhood would have heard how she went out with her daughter.

Those who had not seen would come up to her: 'Miss Johnson, a hear yu went out wid yu Audrey de ada day. Is nice when yu children look out fa yu.' She loved to hear people talk like that, knew they envied her, respected her because of her children's concern.

'Is nuting,' she would often say. 'A train dem up wid de good Lord's help and dem is a credit now.'

But deep down inside she would remember. Feel again the shock, the shame and disappointment when first Delores and then Eena had got pregnant. She had been so sick with disappointment. They had been doing so well at school. How could they let the good for nothing boys trouble them and shame her till she could not hold her head up? She always pushed the thoughts away, that was in the past now. True, some unconscionable people still remembered it, would throw it at her out of spite. But she could live with that, now that Audrey got her job and Carol was doing so well too.

If she loved going to the doctor, Adella hated being there. Hated going up to the glassed-off window. She would stand, conscious of the eyes from the packed waiting-room, having to repeat her name to the patronising young girl on the other side. Then she would sit on an uncomfortable hard blue or orange chair for the long wait. It was always the same at the doctor's. It did not matter how early you came, you always had to wait, fifteen minutes, thirty, sometimes even an hour. Her back always ached with the strain of sitting upright while the endless noise of the ever-present children jarred against her ears.

She never knew anyone there. No one she could exchange some serious gossip with. This time had been no exception. The room was packed with strange faces, all wrapped up in their own misery, their own preoccupation, and the wait before her name was called seemed never-ending. She got up heavily when the girl behind the counter shouted for her, telling Audrey to come with her. Dr Stone was used to seeing one or the other of her children, indeed seemed to prefer it, and she knew that all her friends who saw him brought one of their children if they were around.

'Mrs Johnson,' the doctor said, voice over-bright, remembering her from previous visits. 'How are you?'

Adella shifted in irritation. Why did the man always ask such fofool questions? If she was all right she wouldn't come to see him.

'A sick, docta,' she said bluntly, going through the usual routine. 'A have pain a back, and dung me leg an it shoot up right inna me armpit and tru me neck back.'

The man looked put out, almost as though he thought her rude.

'Dat's de trouble wid dese young docta,' Adella thought grimly. 'Since ole Docta Mason retire an dis new one come fram school tings bad. Ihm doan know what ihm talking bout.'

'What exactly seems to be the trouble?' the man asked, taking a wad of notes stapled together from a beige holder and leafing through it.

'A jus tell yu,' she said impatiently. She often wondered if there was something wrong with this man. Why did he keep asking the same questions over and over again? 'A have a lot a pain an a caan work.'

'That is understandable, Mrs Johnson, but where exactly is the pain?'

Adella wondered if he was trying to make fun of her and she could feel the anger rising inside her when Audrey stepped in, explaining what she had said to the doctor. She could see the girl's annoyance, and she was proud that her children could talk just like white people. Since they started coming with her, things were always better and the man had to listen to them because they could talk like him.

The two of them continued to talk and she looked around the bare room wondering why she bothered to come. She could see that her daughter was not satisfied, felt pride as she insisted on an appointment with a specialist at the hospital. At least she knew that her children would always look out for her. The doctor was reluctant to comply and kept trying to say things would settle down in a few days.

'Dat's what yu did tell me when a fus come,' Adella butted in. 'An dat is long time now, wha yu mean few days?'

The doctor looked uncomfortable. He hesitated, before capitulating. 'Very well,' he said resentfully. 'I will get you an appointment with a consultant at St Thomas's – though I am sure he will confirm what I told you.' As he spoke he wrote rapidly on a piece of paper that had the group practice's name and all the doctors printed on it.

It had been good to see the doctor climb down, to know her daughter had made him do so. She couldn't wait to get home and get on the phone and tell Lisa and the others all about it. Not that they would be surprised, but she knew that inside they would envy her, would wish that they were just as lucky with their children, though they would never let her forget the disappointments that had happened. The way Delores and Eena had come to no good. Yes, it had been nice to boast about the visit to the doctor, but now she had to go down to the hospital. She hated the thought of that, of going to this big man that you needed to get a special written appointment to see. She wished it was Carol going with her, that it wasn't Eena's turn. Eena couldn't talk to them like Audrey or Carol; she would just listen and agree and never asked any of the questions that the other two did. Even so, she meant well and Adella could not hold it against her that she had let her down. After all, she still had Carol, Carol who had never disappointed her, and who she knew would always be with her.

Sounds of movement drifted into her consciousness, bringing her back to the awareness of the smoke-filled room. Adella was surprised to see that it was half-empty, hear more words of goodbye and get well. She had been so wrapped up in her thoughts she hadn't even heard them leaving, but now she looked around eagerly, seeing Mr Peters mopping up the last remnants of gravy on his plate with a piece of hardough bread. She willed him to hurry up and take his leave. She hoped Lisa didn't supply him with any more food. Mr Peters was one of those people who ate anything that was going and if the food kept coming he would never leave her house that night. She felt relief when her friend's head appeared around the door, the wig discarded in the heat and steam of the kitchen. Greyness peppered the soft fine hair cut close to her head. She looked older without the wig, older and more tired, and Adella felt a sense of shock that Lisa too was ageing.

'De food done, Missa Peters,' Lisa said smugly, looking at the man still holding the plate balanced on his fat, distended stomach. Mr Peters looked disappointed, hid it with a smile as he glanced up at the clock.

'Is dat de time, Miss Johnson?' he said, as if the lateness of the hour had only just seeped into his consciousness now that the food had left it. 'A fraid a haffe go, a have so much to do. Yu know what is like on Saturday.'

Adella nodded, hiding her smile. 'Mek ihm eat and gwaan,' she told herself. 'At least ihm gwaan.'

Mr Peters's exit was the cue for the last of the stragglers to leave. Once they had gone the quiet peace of her room reasserted itself. She reached for the television control, pressed it, flooding the room with colours and new sounds, before the front door had even closed on the receding noise of footsteps and conversation.

Some Say it's Madness

Yasmin Issacs

Lord!
Was her cry
she bang her belly
shake her head
drop to her knees
cried all night
till water no longer
fell from her eyes

Prison took her youngest son
death consumed another one
there was no father around
for these boys

Up and down
she tread the ground
talking shadows all around
some say it's madness

I . . . ?
I say it's sadness
she worked from dusk till dawn
had to keep young bellies fed

Then
They told her
they had to let her go
That is how the fretting start
till the pressure burnt her out

Bills!
Bills!
buzzing round her head
pressure hit her right
pressure hit her left

There was no father around
to share this load

Now
She's walking up and down
treading the ground of London town
some say it's madness
I . . .
I say it's sadness
she couldn't take the pain

No one can say she didn't try
wanted the best life for her sons
but there was no father around
to ease this load

She who worked twenty-five hard years
stand on the corner of a London street
A beg you tenpence sir
A beg you tenpence mam

Laughter/anger
raging/laughter
wild eye
beckon from within

What crime did she commit?
They locked her up in some cesspit
no questions asked
some say it's madness
but I say it's pain
she tried in vain
but the pressure sent her down

There was no man around

to ease this load
to share her shame
to father those sons

I say . . . sadness
I say . . . pain.

Cheltenham

Michael Hofmann

The nouveau oil building
spoils the old water town, spook town, old folks' town.
My old parents, like something out of le Carré,
shuffle round the double Georgian square

tracing figures of eight, endless figures of eight,
defected ice dance trainers or frozen old spooks,
patinage, badinage,
reminiscence with silences.

Then a family even if ever there was one:
my mother reads my translation of my father,
who hasn't read aloud since his 'event'.
Darkness falls outside. Inside too.

Ted Hughes is in the small audience,
and afterwards asks my father
whether he ever, like an Innuit,
dreamed of his own defeat and death.

My father, who's heard some questions, but never anything
like this, doesn't know Ted Hughes,

perhaps hears 'idiot', gives an indignant no
in his miraculously clear English.

More laps of the marred green,
the pink sky silts down, a November afternoon
by the clock, his last in England.
The days brutally short; a grumpy early night.

The Godmother

Jan Lo Shinebourne

– Put it in her palm, then she will always have luck.

I did it, just as Mother said, and like magic or luck, the baby opened her palm and took the coin. Then they took it from her and put it with the rest of her money and presents.

Now her father was telephoning. His voice was travelling not just through the telephone line but in my memory.

Outside, the English rain is falling. People are passing by but I can still see his face. He is a jovial and happy man, tall, strong, handsome, a man for a child to idealise.

Am I making him up? Did I use to make him up? He is speaking my name with a voice, an accent and intonation that is not a Georgetown voice, not a New Amsterdam voice, but a Canje voice, the one that was too familiar to be mistaken for any other a mile or ten or twenty or seventy or one hundred miles upriver or up the road. He is sounding just like my father, many years dead now and buried where I was born.

Whenever my mother expected a special visit from a special visitor she would enact laborious rituals of cleansing and cooking. I was witness to this mystery for many years before I performed it myself.

Now, I dust the entire house: ceiling, walls, books, shelves, furniture. Wash all the dust away with soap and water then rinse with perfumed water. If we had carpets they would have been shampooed so I shampoo the carpets. The labour of preparation never wearied Mother. It charged her with energy, and I think I still mimic her psychic behaviour. She was preparing to receive not ordinary people: not just cleaning and cooking; but making something extraordinary happen.

I plan Guyanese food for my long-lost godchild and her parents: calaloo-and-egg soup, pepperpot, ground provisions, salt-fish and boiled eggs in a wash of olive oil with fried onions and tomatoes, fried ochroes, chicken curry and roti, hassa cooked in coconut and rice, chow mein, black cake. From their hiding place, I take precious casareep, rum and cassava bread smuggled into London. Like Mother, I will take out my best china and glasses for these guests. Cooking this meal, perhaps a dream will come true.

I have to travel across London to Brixton to buy sorrel soursop, hassa, mangoes, papaya, wiri-wiri, and ball-of-fire pepper.

The journey is familiar. I can close my eyes and find my way round the underground. I always verify the route before I set off. I always read the underground map at the platform while I am waiting for the train. Then when I am sitting in the carriage I read the smaller replica of the same map on the ceiling of the carriage and I count the stops when the train pulls in and out of stations. Today I ignore these maps.

My feet take me to the market, not my eyes and Brixton landmarks. I don't stop in at the Ritzy for a programme or phone Claudia to see if she is in. I don't stay all day shopping in the market with her and eating lunch. I don't visit Cecil's Bakery for salara and pine tarts. I go straight to Evan's and he gives me the sorrel and soursop he says just came from Trinidad and he tells me I am lucky to get the wiri-wiri and thick-leaf thyme from Guyana because he is growing them himself in his own kitchen. The return journey is the same – no maps.

In winter the kitchen is the coldest room in the house. The draught pours through the door, along the tiled floor, snaps at my heels, and gnaws at my feet. But I am in another world as I cook. In that world, the sun is hot. Naturally, her christening was on a Sunday, at midday.

Sunday was a family day. We would all be together at home, living in slow time with the newspapers to read and lunch to cook and eat at leisure. It is the one day Father and Mother sleep in the afternoon. They sleep outdoors in the hammocks under the mango trees. This memory is very easy to live. I slide into it so easily, like a contented child going to sleep between clean sheets fresh from drying in the sun and fresh air. Sometimes, it is this easy to live in the past and present.

Happy, I begin to peel the onions, boil the water and heat the oil. The clock reminds me I have three hours to cook the meal before the Allens are here. When he telephoned, I could not remember their names. He was Joseph, his wife was Cynthia, my god-daughter was Yvette. Now their faces in my mind have their rightful names. The placing of the names to faces brings with it the placing of people to places. The school, the church, the sugar factory, the overseer quarters, the court and police stations – these are parts of the past to dislike because they are places for colonising people.

The christening is as bright as the sun was on the day. I see it as clearly as I see the ingredients of my cooking. The steam from the pots forms a mist. It rises in the air and I see more of the christening. The intensely rich scent of frying ochroes also rises. It is very very hot but the men are wearing suits and ties. I pour the boiling water over the salt fish. I toss cloves and cinnamon sticks, orange peel and dark sugar into the hot, scarlet sorrel liquid.

I can see my father's trunk again. It was a most ancient possession of his. I am a child again, struggling to drag it from under the bed. The handle is thin, black metal, very loose in my small hands. This trunk came from somewhere far away. Every time I pull it towards me, from under my parents' bed, I think

I am pulling a country towards me. My father always tells me which country it came from but I always forget which. He came from three, and more. He was born in one, one brought him here and several adopted him. My imagination inhabits his trunk. I like to pull it from its hiding place and open it. I always think I never know what I am going to find. But whenever I open it, there are always the same things there: a strange, shining black suit with a high-collared jacket; and a shining white shirt with a stiff collar and large cuffs. I have never seen him dressed in this suit but he keeps it in the best condition. It was not a suit for wearing. It never left the trunk except to be cleaned and aired. When I was no longer a child, someone told me it was his father's suit. My grandfather may have made it, since he was a tailor. There were papers in the trunk I would secretly play with because he said they were very important – yellowed, browning paper tied in pink string. The letters he and my mother wrote each other when they were courting were kept there. Sometimes, my mother kept a dress for best there but not for long. All our birth certificates were kept in the trunk and mothballs too, to preserve everything.

We rarely had occasion for dressing up, only births, marriages and deaths when our Sunday best came out from the trunk under the bed, out of mothballs. Special occasions smelt of mothballs, of best soap, talcum, perfumes and new dresses. We always cleaned and washed ourselves and everything else besides for the newborn, the newly wed and the dead.

The smell of ripe plantain is strongest in the pot of boiling cassava, yam, and sweet potatoes. For the curry, I have to blend fresh pepper and *jeera* very lightly, and the gravy has to be extremely thin. I must use only one fresh tomato and a leaf of thyme. Add water at the very last. I can see my mother dip the spoon into a *karahi* of boiling curry, trickle the gravy from a height so it cools in the air in its passage to the palm of her hand. I am in her kitchen again. She would never taste from the spoon, only from her palm. I trickle *metagee* into my palm and taste from hers. I am cooking for ghosts, spirits. The smell of my food is attracting them. For this very reason, there is no cooked food on the day of a funeral. The rituals of cooking, the opening of trunks smelling of mothballs, soap, perfume and talcum powder – the christening was part of it.

Now I can see myself at the christening. All the girls are in organdie dresses. Mine is the palest colour of pink. I am wearing a small, white pillbox hat and white gloves. I am not just any child today, I am a godmother. My mother and father are there, and the Allens, and the baby, all the village. I can see the table, full of food. Today, I am cooking the meal that was prepared for the christening.

My relatives arrive before my guests of honour. The scent of the food puts them in a good mood, makes them forget the cold weather, and stirs their memory.

– The Allens lived in Cumberland all their lives until they went to live in Georgetown in 1966. People were always leaving the country areas for Georgetown but I never thought they would leave.

– And they never came back?

– Oh yes!

– But I never saw Yvette again.

– When they came to visit, you were always at school.

– No one told me when they visited.

– After the race riots, Joseph joined the new government and stopped coming to Berbice. But he always wrote to your parents, he kept in touch.

– I never knew that. I used to ask after Yvette, and nobody ever told me that.

– There was an English priest who did the christening. Father Jones. Is he still in Berbice?

– He was from the North of England. He was a paedophile. Everybody knew about it. I would not have him christen my child.

Secrets are the difficult parts of memory, especially secrets you are still not permitted to know, still not permitted to speak, secrets that were knowledge and power to protect the ones in control. You dare to speak them and they silence you with public shaming and ridicule. Secrets, knowledge and power were for closing and opening ranks, keeping in those who never tell and keeping out the ones who do.

Father Jones is dead now. We do not live in his parish. Our jobs do not depend on baptisings, christenings, mass, evensongs and funerals. His secret is not important any more. They can tell it now. But God is not dead. God might hear. Be careful. Whisper. Don't discuss it. Say it once. We will pretend we did not hear. There are places where there are echoes we cannot drown – places of the past, places of the mind, places of memory, places of the heart.

They dare to say now what could not be said then, and now when the doorbell rings I will open the front door and it will be as if memory is really opening and the past and present will be rejoined.

The doorbell is ringing.

Certainly, their faces hardly bear a resemblance to the faces in my memory. They are not the handsome, warm couple in my memory. They greet us with religious words. They are born-again Christians. Their mission is conversion. They say grace before the meal, and Joseph behaves like a god. He expects the women to wait on him. Yvette and Cynthia defer to him; he is a man of power. I did not see it. He was a policeman.

Yvette and her mother hardly eat or speak, only when he prompts them. If they dared to speak, what would happen? Would they be silenced and humiliated? They would be disgraced publicly for not keeping secrets. Did I expect the ghosts from the past would rise like Lazarus from the dead? Does memory survive the ashes of history? Now, Guyana was the second-poorest country in the world after Haiti and malaria had returned. Guyana was no longer the bread-basket of the Caribbean, no longer had the highest literacy rate in the region, our political culture was in ruins, we could not return home

– so the conversation went, round and round the table, and Joseph nodded like a president. They ask him questions about Guyana, the kind of anxious questions emigrants ask, and Joseph answers them.

– How are things in Guyana?

– Oh very good.

– Are the police still killing the opposition?

– Oh no.

– Has the race politics stopped?

– Oh yes.

– Are the roads improving?

– Oh yes.

– Has malaria really come back?

– Oh no.

– Is there still a food shortage?

– Oh no.

– You are a good public relations man for the country!

– Oh yes indeed I am. After all, I am the Chief of Police in Berbice.

Only the fruit salad and black cake remained, the last fragments of the dream meal. They were still talking about Guyana, the politics, power struggles and hatreds without end. Joseph dictated the conversation. They could share no other memory with him. To me, he was neither one party nor the other, he was both. His power was all.

I don't know which I was when I decided to turn to Yvette – my psychic mother or my young self; perhaps both. Before they ate the black cake I had to perform the ritual I knew my mother would, though it was for the child Yvette and I had been. Perhaps it was something to do with my father's trunk but my voice was speaking although I could see that Joseph did not like it. I was telling Yvette I was sorry I never got to see her again, and I opened her hand and placed in it the pair of earrings I had bought for her. I knew this was the right ritual.

Her father spoke directly to her. – Yvette you are very lucky indeed to have such a nice godmother. I hope you are grateful. You know, the young people are never grateful. You are very lucky to be born to have such a godmother. Those are good gold earrings, worth plenty. Let me see them.

He did not return the earrings to Yvette. We cleared the table. Joseph would not help. He threw his arm over the back of the chair and crossed his legs – making himself more comfortable.

The time came for them to leave and Joseph asked to speak to me privately. I took him to the kitchen.

– Maybe you live in England too long, and you don't remember. But it is the custom for the godparent to also give a present of money to the godchild father.

– My present is for Yvette, not for you.

I clear away the remains of my dream dinner. I wash the plates, cooker, and walls and surfaces of the kitchen. I am certain I detect a lingering scent of mothballs in the air.

The Sacrificial Lamb

Sindiwe Magona

Before Siziwe was fully awake, the receiver – cold, hard and decidedly unfriendly – jabbed at the not-fully-awake flesh in the hollow between her shoulder, the pillow, and her ear. She did not remember how it had got there. There was a vague memory of the phone ringing; but even as she struggled to hold it, sleep eluded that memory so that it slipped right through her eyelashes and left her in frustrating confusion where there was a tantalising overlap between reality and dream. But, of course, the phone must have rung, otherwise why had she picked up the receiver? Not that she remembered doing that either. She knew she must have done so, though. And now, to the remote *peep-peep* announcing an overseas call she mumbled 'Hello?' – relief washing through her. It was not the police, calling about her daughter, Fezi. She glanced at the bedside clock-radio thinking, *where on earth is that child?* Just then, a voice came through the line.

'Hello? Is that you, Sisi?'

'Yes, it's me. Who is this?' She no longer recognised the voices; that grown her nieces sounded to her, whether on the phone or in their infrequent letters. No doubt, Siziwe was sure, distance and nostalgia accelerated and augmented the changes she perceived: with them . . . with her.

'Is everything all right?' she asked, a new anxiousness replacing the earlier worry. What if her mother were ill? What would she do then? Go home? Or sweat it out here till . . . ? What would be the point of going then? But even as she argued with herself in her mind, she knew: of course, she would go.

'Sisi, it's me, Nozipho. Everything is fine; after a manner of speaking, that is. What else can we say?'

'What has happened? Is Ma OK?'

'Mama is OK. She says can you call her back?' And before she could say yea or nay, there was a clang and the line went dead.

She leapt out of bed and went to make herself a cup of coffee. Might as well make myself comfortable, she thought. Calling Cala was never a simple operation. The call had to go via the telephone exchange – and the Cala Telephone Exchange was slack, inept, and often the lines were down.

The coffee burned her throat the way she liked it. Her mind went back to that long-ago day, the day she had not known would be the last when she would see her father. One would have thought there was a way of feeling, of sensing, of somehow presaging such an event; a kind of body seismograph, reading her the foreshadowing symptoms. But no, despite her great love for him, she had looked at her father, talked to him and then walked away from him with a casual goodbye. Next thing she knew, the sturdy tree that had given her shade from scorching sun and shelter from the storms of life had fallen.

On the second attempt, much to her amazement, she got through.

'Hello, Sisi? It's still me, Nozipho. There's something I forgot to tell you.'

'Yes, Zips? What is it?' She tried not to think of the money she was paying, listening to idle chatter. Sheer waste.

'I have written you a letter and given it to Bhuti Wallace. He is coming there and we gave him your address and telephone number. Please, Sisi, do respond positively to my request. Do not disappoint me. You know I have no one else I can depend on.'

'What is it?'

'No, I can't say it now. Wait till you get the letter.'

'That bad, is it?'

'No, it's not!' A burst of thrilling laughter fractured her speech. 'Sisi, I must get off this phone.' Siziwe knew what was coming. She could hear her mother grumbling in the background. 'Ma is giving me her wicked look. You know her. Bye, Sis.'

'Bye!' Had she heard? wondered Siziwe, for her 'bye' collided with her mother's 'Hello, Siziwe!' as belaboured breathing replaced Nozipho's breezy prattle on the line.

'Hello, Ma! Are you all right?'

'Siziwe, my child, the Lord keeps on minding us. But the devil is also busy, derailing us every which way we turn.'

'What is the matter?' And she had the presence of mind to stop short of adding the 'now' burning the tip of her tongue. But the irritation seared her brain. Can they never call just to see how I am doing? Is each telephone call always only going to be about some catastrophe?

'MaTolo is in hospital.' There was a slight pause; no doubt, her mother was waiting to hear her reaction to this piece of news. But Siziwe waited too . . . Whatever she said would end up upsetting her mother; she did not seem to ever come up with anything kind to say about her eldest brother; a complete washout of a man.

'Our kind neighbour, Majola, took him to Zala Hospital in his car.'

'What is the matter with him?' This time she was forced to say something since her mother had gone silent on her.

'We really don't know what happened to him. Saturday, early evening, some people came and told us that he was lying, face down, at the corner of Sandile Street and Xhalanga Street. When we got there, we couldn't even recognise him. Half his face had caved in, probably hit with a brick – what they call the Wonder Loaf here. He was completely covered in blood that had already caked. As yet, no witnesses have come forward to say who did what to him.'

'But what about him? What does he say happened?'

'He can't even say one word, my child. All he does is groan. He does not even recognise those who have been to see him. I, myself, have not been to see him; could not bring myself to go . . . no, I just couldn't go and see him looking like that – like a corpse.'

'I am sorry, Ma. I'm really sorry.' And, to her surprise, she realised that she meant what she said. Of course, she was only sorry for the worry MaTolo's troubles always caused her mother. Her sisters and brothers were slowly killing the poor woman; ageing her and wearing her down fast with all the troubles they visited on her: drunken brawls, job loss caused by bad work habits, unemployment due to lack of qualifications, and a host of other causes besides. The same problems that plagued everybody else in the black townships . . . why did she allow these things to disarrange her? Why would her family be any different to all the others?

Once more, her father's words of farewell led her to a decision. Often had she wondered whether they were a blessing or a curse. '*Mna, kuphela eyam intlungu yeyenyama*. My pain is only that of the flesh.' Thus had he thanked her – or, perhaps ordered is more like it – for those words had forever after directed her actions . . . especially towards her mother.

Even so far away, in this strange land, among people whose ways were stranger still, she still heard those words. *While other men in this ward cry, not because of physical pain but because they do not know what their children will eat that very day or a man's family is being thrown out of the house because they owe rent money, I am at peace because you, my daughter, see to the needs of the family.*

'So, we thought we should ask for some help from you, my child.' Her mother's voice broke into Siziwe's reflections. 'I know we are forever bothering you with all these stupid problems these children are always getting themselves into. But, what else can we do? Who else can we turn to?'

There was a moment's awkward silence, the unspoken

words *'Now that your father is no longer here'* heavy between them.

Had her father, in thanking her for giving the family financial support, in fact appointed her his surrogate?

'You must help us, my child.'

'Of course, Ma.' She was embarrassed. 'What did you think I should do?' Of course, that too was just formality. She knew exactly why they had called her . . . why they always and invariably called her: money.

'Whatever little money you can send us will help. We have to go to the hospital to see him. What would people think – and how would he feel? We can't abandon him there all on his own . . . and at a time like this.'

The next morning, a Monday, she got up half an hour earlier than she usually did. She liked to start her work-day punctually and purposefully; more so Mondays. She was dressed and getting ready to leave when a groggy voice asked her, 'Want a cup of coffee, Mother, dearest?' Siziwe did not trust herself to say a word in reply. But the look she gave Fezi was more eloquent than anything she could have come up with.

By nine, she had made the transfer from Chemical Bank to her mother's account with Volkskas Bank in Elliot, the nearest town to Cala that boasted such facilities as banks. Over a cup of coffee, she thought about Fezi. Hope she makes it to class. When the girl had eventually found her way home the previous night, Siziwe had no idea. Mama's call had come well after two; nearer three than two, in fact. And after the call she had gone to see whether Fezi was in her room. Not getting a reply to her knock, she'd gently pushed the door open. And the serene bed so incensed her, blind tears rolled down her cheeks before she even knew she was crying. How many times had she told the girl, 'All I ask is that when you are busy having fun, I should not be lying awake in bed, wondering if the next telephone call will be the police, telling me you've been shot or strangled; raped, robbed or pushed in front of a moving train.'

But her daughter behaved as though the mother were a big fusspot. As if these horrendous things were not happening, every day, in the city where they made their home. As if they were something Siziwe just conjured up to frighten herself and use to chain her daughter to the house. But then, that is the privilege of the young: the singular lack of fear of death, their complete belief in their own immortality.

After work, she stopped for Happy Hour at the Ritz, a cosy little restaurant patronised by the foreigners because of its international cuisine. She was meeting Nomsa, a fellow South African who had lived in New York for almost thirty years. As usual, before long, their talk was about home, the country, its people and, more particularly, their families.

'Hey, Siziwe, do you want to hear the latest about my crazy family?' When she nodded, knowing full well that whether she wanted to hear Nomsa's news or not, hear it she would, Nomsa told her, 'My sister is unbelievable! Do you remember her?' There was a pause, but not for long. Nomsa answered herself, 'I've told you so much about her, you must. This is a woman, over forty, who dropped out of university. She is so bright, she had a first-class matric pass, passed the first two years in college with flying colours, but then, despite our advice, despite our protestations, decided she wanted to get married.

'Well, of course, that didn't last. Two children. No profession. Too proud of "My University Education" to do any job unless it is not beneath Madam's status.

'Doesn't she call me, collect? Do you know how many times I have told her not to do that? Unless, of course, it is absolutely necessary: a death or grave illness, something of that nature.

'But no, each time she goes on a binge, she remembers she has this rich sister in America and calls me, but I have to pay for those calls. She is not that drunk she forgets that an overseas telephone call costs a lot of money.'

'I also had a call from home yesterday ... or, early this

morning, I should say,' Siziwe interrupted, still smarting from the hole the morning's withdrawal had made in her savings.

'Ah, but your family, listen to me, your family is reasonable. Mine? Mine is something else, believe me!'

Siziwe started to tell her about her mother's call. Then, somehow, Fezi's staying out the whole night – 'for she must have come in well after four' – came in and took centre stage.

'I miss having my family help me with the children. You know, at home, this wouldn't be just my problem alone. Her uncles, my brothers, would help. So would Mama. She would talk to her, show her how to behave herself.'

'Yes, that's true,' replied Nomsa. 'Our extended family is truly a blessing. One is never alone, whatever travails one is facing.'

Siziwe nodded, thinking of her mother and the strength she drew from her, just knowing she was there. Whatever would she do if anything happened to her mother? She told Nomsa, 'You know something? Often, when I'm troubled, I will pick up the phone and call Mama. But, when I hear her voice, realise how far she is, I ask myself: why should I bother her with my little troubles? She would only worry. And the Lord knows, she needs that like she needs a second head on her shoulders. And, do you know what? Just hearing her voice, just knowing she is there, I already feel better.'

'Remember what you said, some time ago?' Nomsa was looking at her expectantly.

'No. What?' What of the numerous things she had said to Nomsa over the years was she referring to? Well, she would just have to remind her. Siziwe waited, eyebrows raised in question.

'You said, "Those of us who are supposed to have 'made it' are the ones whom, for whatever reason, the ancestors have chosen as sacrificial lambs for the family!" '

'Oh that? Sure, but this is slaughter! And when will I save for old age? Things are changing and I would be a big fool if I expect my children to look after me when I am retired.'

'Very true, my friend. But, as you yourself have said, we make it so that the family may endure, despite the unbearable trauma visited on it. How else would so many of us have survived apartheid . . . were it not for those who, despite unimaginably overwhelming odds, "*made it*"?'

Letter to Jakarta

Aamer Hussein

When I think of home, it's not Jakarta I remember, but Grandfather's home in Yogyakarta. That chicken we used to eat with our fingers, soaked in the taste of jackfruit, sticky rice we licked off our fingers and those small hot chillies to balance the sweetness. The food here is terrible, but we've found a Malay hostel where we can get a decent meal – not marvellous, but all right. Elleke doesn't cook much. On the third night after our arrival she said she'd make some nasi goreng and we were curious to see how she'd handle it. Yati went into the kitchen to see if she could help her – which she doesn't much like, anyway, and she was decorating the rice with slices of meat from a cellophane packet. What's that, Yati asked. Ham, of course, came the answer. But we don't eat ham, Yati said, or any other form of pork. So move it, Elleke said, and eat the other stuff. There's lots of prawns and vegetables and egg in there.

We couldn't do that.

Papa said in Bahasa, as if Elleke couldn't understand: Come on kids, it won't kill you, your mother used to feed it to you when you were kids. Is that true, Mama? Did you feed us pork in Paris?

We have the same sort of problem in the lavatory. There's no bidet and I took an old vinegar bottle I'd scavenged from the kitchen so that we could keep ourselves clean but in a day or so it had disappeared. I found another one and hid it behind the loo. Elleke decided to have it out with me. This isn't Jakarta, you know, she said. There isn't anyone here to mop up your spills. I kicked that last bottle over, drenched the carpet and nearly broke my leg. Can't you just have a bath if you're so fastidious about your body? God knows you aren't a terribly tidy pair.

She says everything with a sort of indulgent smile and I can see her point in a way, I suppose, but Mama, there isn't a shower in the bathroom and you have to soak yourself in a bath. I can get away with sneaking a glass in to wash my body off with after soaking but she's got some sort of obsession about water. One drop anywhere drives her crazy. And Yati's veil. You should see how she handles that. On Sunday morning she came down to breakfast in jeans with a plain white scarf on her head and Elleke gave her that saccharine smile and said: Yetty (that's how she pronounces it), Yetty darling, you should lose some weight before you put on such tight things. Your bottom is far too big and when you wear that scarf – it looks so incongruous and it does rather defeat the point somehow, don't you think?

Yati handles Elleke far better than I do. She's found some sympathetic 'sisters' in college and a girl from Kelantan took her to an Indian shop where she bought herself yards of stuff which they stitched up into an adapted sarong kebaya, matching and loose and flowing, so you should see Yati now, she looks a bit like a colourful nun. She says she feels good about it, distinctive somehow, as if she's painted on the parameters of her identity and people know how far to go with her. She calls it her gentle armour.

Yati's generally more resourceful than I am. She's found herself a prayer group and a discussion group and she attends classes in history and political theory because she says faith should be intellectual as well as visceral and in any case this ex-centre of empire segregates discourses and it's all-important for us as Javanese and Indonesians to introduce ourselves into the discussion rather than to hide in corners pleading cultural distinction or adopt Arab gestures and rituals in some kind of false identification of Arab culture with Islam. You should see the debates that go on in abandoned college classrooms, in cafés and in hostels and even on the pavements on the street. We were used to hearing our Muslim companions criticising the capitalist way as detrimental to spiritual progress: here you can meet people who praise dictators and kings who squash their poor because they deal in the letter of the law and follow the precepts of the faith. Our Sheikh always called those leaders semi-infidels; he said they were just as much to blame for our plight today as those radical innovators who told us to throw away all our good beliefs along with the old superstitions and pushed the kind of nationalism down our throat that fostered isolation from our brothers and identification with satanic powers. Of course in Ilmuddin Salam's terms satan – I emphasise the small s – is only a metaphor for those powers we carry within ourselves that reflect and continue the evil powers contained in the universe and released through acts of war and injustice and violence.

Other groups analyse Islam in terms of politics of a semi-Marxist sort, picking up the flaws in all debates and filling in the gaps with enlightened sayings from the Koran and other, later texts. Sometimes I feel they sound too much like the bigots they criticise, but I can see their point; they say that since economics determines our worldly consciousness, we're trapped in a prison of spiritual poverty that is a symptom of our abject position in the hierarchy of power.

After one meeting – we were addressed by a European scholar – I met a Swedish girl who's doing her PhD in Islamic studies. She asked me out for a coffee because she wanted Indonesian perspectives on Islam. We fell into the way of meeting once or even twice a week and the third week she said she'd cook something for me. I went to her house – a hundred miles away from Papa's house, it seemed, in a suburb of unpainted doors and untrimmed hedges. She laid out some dips that were tasty and filling though they were cold and I felt like something hot, but then she brought out some meatballs with nuts in them that were quite delicious. We drank coffee and she told me the story of her life. She's in her late twenties and already divorced.

I spoke a little bit about our life at home, Mama, about you and Yati and the house and the college and Rendra's recitals. When I came to the situation here at Papa's I hesitated: you know how you've always said that I seemed to be more grandmother's child than yours with my Javanese reticence, whereas you and Yati had inherited some gene that made Grandfather such an outspoken extrovert. But talking about one's intimate experiences hurts; and Europeans have a way of picking up what's unsaid and assuming somehow that you're hiding it all from yourself, which of course I'm not. She spoke of my life in terms of paternal deprivation and maternal domination and said that I longed for order and authority and that was the reason I'd become a neo-Muslim, but the natural gentleness of my personality took me towards a father substitute who was less abrasive than the beliefs he represented. I've never really looked upon Ilmuddin as a father substitute and her interpretation – it's what the Sheikh would call over-interpretation, or the danger of agnostic theory – somehow seems to leave out Yati and her reactions, which are similar at least in their essence to mine.

It was midnight when we finished talking. She said I'd better stay the night and began rummaging in her cupboard for blankets while I, in some trepidation of their reaction, dialled Papa and Elleke's number – I'd never stayed out so late before and certainly never all night. Elleke answered. Her tone was irritated but tolerant. She said that Papa'd begun to panic because he thought that in these rough times and rough places I might have been taken for an Indian with my dark skin and attacked by hoodlums. She said she'd explained to him that I must be hanging out with one chapter or another of the Muslim brethren and decided to stay over. I wish, she said, that you'd find a girlfriend – I almost wondered whether she'd guessed that I was with a girl.

Viveca – my friend's name – called out to me to help her carry out some pillows from her bedroom. She'd already changed, she wore pyjamas, so unlike your silk nightgowns or Yati's. Her bed was unmade and littered with clothes. She's not very tall for a Scandinavian but, Mama, she's almost my height. As I reached for the pillows she stood behind me. I could feel her brown hair brush my face and her breath, too. If you like, she said, you can just pop into my bed.

I always thought popping in meant dropping in to visit someone. I suppose that's what I did. I visited her. A strange country. Her eyes are green and big. She was surprised that I had hair on my chest and legs because my hands are nearly hairless and she'd thought that all Javanese were smooth. At first I was nervous, too impetuous to cover my inexperience, but she saw me through. In the morning I was shy of her but she was already in the kitchen spreading the remains of last night's supper dips on biscuits and toast. Hi, she said when I walked in. The kettle's boiling. Just take down some cups and make some coffee. There's tea, too, if that's what you prefer.

It's funny, Mama, she always says: would you prefer some coffee? Would you prefer a biscuit? without adding another clause. I can't correct her, her English is otherwise so much better than mine. But you've passed on your love of words to me, Mama, of sentences and their structure and syntax. It's the meanings that I worry about now, though, and I can't seem to get to the meaning of this relationship. We certainly don't have a future. At the moment I'm not even sure I want to stay on here to attend college when I've done my English certificate. So I keep on writing to you in my head or on scraps of paper or in this notebook that I keep by my pillow with the title *Letters to Mama*, knowing these are things I can't admit to you in the formal Javanese missives you seem to receive from me every Wednesday morning, but telling you about them seems to clear my head, even though you may not know what I'm talking about. Because I know that you would have an answer that would help me to decide even in contradiction to you.

*

What do they say in Jakarta about this war, Mama? You should hear the students at school, in the cafeteria, in the mosque. Some of them believe Saddam is our friend, our brother, even our saviour. Others defend America: after all, they say, whatever its reasons, you can't justify the invasion of a tiny country by a superior power and America has at least led the world to fulfil its moral obligations. Brothers fight with each other over the ethical and the political issues of the war. I wonder what our Ilmuddin would say: sometimes I feel that his lessons were too gentle, too mild, and I have to search within myself for answers. One thing's for certain: it isn't a Muslim war. You should hear the different Arab groups in conflict with each other, not to mention the Iranians and the Indians and the Pakistanis.

When I first went to the mosque, I found it strange to say my prayers surrounded by so many different races. There's a massive group of Africans and you can see Lebanese and Cypriots and Syrians so blond and blue-eyed I took them at first for European converts to Islam. Then I thought of it as a kind of universal fraternity of Muslims and suspended that nagging historical question I'd always asked myself: is it our religious beliefs that have exposed us to ridicule, subjugation, decadence and loss of identity? And I opted instead for a waking dream – perhaps this fraternity, paralleled by the sorority I see among Yati's group of Muslim women, veiled and unveiled, black, brown or white – I thought that may be the answer; no, not the answer but an answer, the suspension of national and ethnic differences in search of common causes, united within a newly defined frontierless land of Islam, an Islam free of the despotism derived from centuries of subjection and distortion.

But what can you say when after our Friday prayers the groups separate – the Gulf people and the pro-America Egyptians and some Lebanese walk away swearing at the Iraqis and damning the Palestinians? Even the Arabs themselves – the thinking ones – accept however quietly the abdication of their peoples from the leadership of the Muslims. The Muslim dream,

Mama, has no country, except in our hearts. Mama, this isn't even a question of religion – it touches for me the question of the very nature of God. In our arguments – Yati is always more vociferous than I am – the Chinese and the Indians seem to be more logical than some of us. Then, again, divided in their opinions, but I'm talking about the ones who stand against the war. It's a Third World cause, they shout, it could be us tomorrow, and loving Saddam doesn't come into it, he may be the butcher he's said to be but surely he's a creation of these very monsters that are now out to destroy him? So it's a question of nations and peoples and economics but our faith seems to be trapped in the middle of it all. You should hear some of the stuff on television, Mama, even Papa nearly got sick the other night into his whisky when an interviewer rounded up some Muslims and pushed them to reject the reasons for war – and you know what the outcome was? Over-interpretation again. You should have heard the men they chose, Mama, none of them defended Saddam, but the interviewer announced at the end that there was an Islamic fifth column in the heart of this country that was out to subvert the very basis of its democratic and egalitarian rules. And all they'd said was that the systematic destruction of any country by an amassed confederacy of superpowers was excessive in these times. It was wrong to bring religion into it, Mama, wrong of this man and wrong of the warmongers who call upon us to kill each other in the name of God.

We have learned to confuse countries with their ideologies and the spirit of people with the doctrines of their rulers, Viveca said. She supports my ambivalent stand against the war, though she says it has as much to do with her own European guilt about the cold use of advanced technology in the name of just causes as it does with her fascination with the heritage of Islam and the Arab culture and language that she still holds lie at its centre.

As for me, Mama, I continue to believe in that dream enclosed in the song you used to sing to us, about a world without nations or borders, but while these borders exist what can we do but shoulder the distinctions imposed upon us by history and race and culture and all those externals beyond our control, what can we do but examine them and extract from them what we can to make sense of our lives? I don't know if my religion is part of my identity or my identity has been written into my religion so long ago that it's impossible to extricate myself from its demands without tearing myself apart.

Mama:

Ours is a group that has united in spite of its differences to call out for an end to war. The snow is thick on the ground and yet we stand here in protest against injustice. Today we stand together under the banner of what some of us may choose to call the message of the eternal God and others may defend as the abstract principles that we believe emanate from Him. But today, Mama, it doesn't matter. Do you remember those old Javanese poems that spoke of the dwelling-place of God? Viveca showed me a strand running right through the utterances of the mystics that says there's no need to visit the Holy Places, no need to kiss the Black Stone of Mecca, if He lives in your heart.

Mama, the speakers come from all walks of life, there's a Kurd asking us not to use his people's name as another tool of exchange, and a Christian woman with an accent I can hardly understand whose main concern is the survival of the children, and a youth from the north of this country whose seventeen-year-old brother has gone to the war and may die. Suspend ideologies, they seem to say even as they dissect the beliefs that fuel these conflicts and the materialistic non-beliefs that lie behind them. Viveca is weeping. Yati has clapped so hard that her brown face has reddened with emotion. The snowflakes fall on our bare heads as we seek shelter under dripping trees. The city is almost silent – snowdrifts so deep have formed that walking is a hazard. And yet we walk, and yet we stand, and we stand here in the biting wind and we march to light a fire of justice and to extinguish the fire of war . . .

There's a large gang of men approaching, Mama. We can hear their voices in the distance, coming closer, at first we think it may be a chant against the war but it sounds like a drunken litany of names, it's menacing somehow, threatening, they come closer, it's a group of men, some of them carry bottles and flags, there's a strong smell of drink from them, they're drinking, Mama, and shouting the names of places I don't know, Viveca grips my arm, her fingers are urgent, I can make out some of their words now, it's a confused diatribe: Butchers, Wogs, Muslims, Sodom, Sod'em, Fuck black bastards, Ay-Rabs, we don't want your sort here.

Who began the fight, Mama? They're attacking us with bottles. The Palestinian group has taken charge of us, they're forming a barricade against the intruders. Members of one of the left-wing groups have moved forward too, parroting the ugly sounds of the green-clad gang with new words. Two men have gone down already, and there's a strange knot of three men on their feet, heads together, entangled hideously. A bleeding youth has grabbed his adversary's bottle and is attacking at random, determined to draw blood for blood. Where are the upholders of the law, Mama? Are they on some hidden margin of our small demonstration, protecting some other splintered group? Our assailants have grabbed a girl, Mama, and torn off her scarf. She's struggling but from where I am I can smell her fear. I move forward. Viveca restrains me. Stop, screams the pressure of her fingers. But Yati's broken away, she's running towards her friend, she's kicking at an attacker, look, Mama, she's bleeding, I've got to go, there's a knife flashing somewhere, I've got to go, Viveca's with me though I try to push her back, I'm nearly there, Mama, Yati, oh, Yati, she's bleeding, someone has me from behind, I don't know whose bodies these are, pressing against me, I push against them at random, here I am, Mama, nearly there, a hand grabs my hair, someone's stinking mouth on my face, take this, wog bastard, a kick in the small of my back, I'm struggling, a fist in my teeth, Mama, something's bursting, I can hear the explosion in my head, I smash at my adversary, feel hard bone splintering under my fist, help me, my sister's pinned under one of them on the ground, bottles fly all around us, a knee in my belly, in my ribs, I'm face to face with my killer, yes, Mama, I'm bleeding inside, a bitter liquid fills my mouth, Yati, Viveca all fading, I fall into someone's arms, I recognise her smell, Mama, I'm gone

The Management of Grief

Bharati Mukherjee

A woman I don't know is boiling tea the Indian way in my kitchen. There are a lot of women I don't know in my kitchen, whispering, and moving tactfully. They open doors, rummage through the pantry, and try not to ask me where things are kept. They remind me of when my sons were small, on Mother's Day or when Vikram and I were tired, and they would make big, sloppy omelets. I would lie in bed pretending I didn't hear them.

Dr Sharma, the treasurer of the Indo-Canada Society, pulls me into the hallway. He wants to know if I am worried about money. His wife, who has just come up from the basement with a tray of empty cups and glasses, scolds him. 'Don't bother Mrs Bhave with mundane details.' She looks so monstrously pregnant her baby must be days overdue. I tell her she shouldn't be carrying heavy things. 'Shaila,' she says, smiling, 'this is the fifth.' Then she grabs a teenager by his shirt-tails. He slips his Walkman off his head. He has to be one of her four children, they have the same domed and dented foreheads. 'What's the official word now?' she demands. The boy slips the headphones back on. 'They're acting evasive, Ma. They're saying it could be an accident or a terrorist bomb.'

All morning, the boys have been muttering, Sikh Bomb,

Sikh Bomb. The men, not using the word, bow their heads in agreement. Mrs Sharma touches her forehead at such a word. At least they've stopped talking about space debris and Russian lasers.

Two radios are going in the dining room. They are tuned to different stations. Someone must have brought the radios down from my boys' bedrooms. I haven't gone into their rooms since Kusum came running across the front lawn in her bathrobe. She looked so funny, I was laughing when I opened the door.

The big TV in the den is being whizzed through American networks and cable channels.

'Damn!' some man swears bitterly. 'How can these preachers carry on like nothing's happened?' I want to tell him we're not that important. You look at the audience, and at the preacher in his blue robe with his beautiful white hair, the potted palm trees under a blue sky, and you know they care about nothing.

The phone rings and rings. Dr Sharma's taken charge. 'We're with her,' he keeps saying. 'Yes, yes, the doctor has given calming pills. Yes, yes, pills are having necessary effect.' I wonder if pills alone explain this calm. Not peace, just a deadening quiet. I was always controlled, but never repressed. Sound can reach me, but my body is tensed, ready to scream. I hear their voices all around me. I hear my boys and Vikram cry, 'Mommy, Shaila!' and their screams insulate me, like headphones.

The woman boiling water tells her story again and again. 'I got the news first. My cousin called from Halifax before 6 a.m., can you imagine? He'd gotten up for prayers and his son was studying for medical exams and he heard on a rock channel that something had happened to a plane. They said first it had disappeared from the radar, like a giant eraser just reached out. His father called me, so I said to him, what do you mean, "something bad"? You mean a hijacking? And he said, *behn*, there is no confirmation of anything yet, but check with your neighbors because a lot of them must be on that plane. So I called poor Kusum straight away. I knew Kusum's husband and daughter were booked to go yesterday.'

Kusum lives across the street from me. She and Satish had moved in less than a month ago. They said they needed a bigger place. All these people, the Sharmas and friends from the Indo-Canada Society had been there for the housewarming. Satish and Kusum made homemade tandoori on their big gas grill and even the white neighbors piled their plates high with that luridly red, charred, juicy chicken. Their younger daughter had danced,and even our boys had broken away from the Stanley Cup telecast to put in a reluctant appearance. Everyone took pictures for their albums and for the community newspapers – another of our families had made it big in Toronto – and now I wonder how many of those happy faces are gone. 'Why does God give us so much if all along He intends to take it away?' Kusum asks me.

I nod. We sit on carpeted stairs, holding hands like children. 'I never once told him that I loved him,' I say. I was too much the well-brought-up woman. I was so well brought up I never felt comfortable calling my husband by his first name.

'It's all right,' Kusum says. 'He knew. My husband knew. They felt it. Modern young girls have to say it because what they feel is fake.'

Kusum's daughter, Pam, runs in with an overnight case. Pam's in her McDonald's uniform. 'Mummy! You have to get dressed!' Panic makes her cranky. 'A reporter's on his way here.'

'Why?'

'You want to talk to him in your bathrobe?' She starts to brush her mother's long hair. She's the daughter who's always in trouble. She dates Canadian boys and hangs out in the mall, shopping for tight sweaters. The younger one, the goody-goody one according to Pam, the one with a voice so sweet that when she sang *bhajans* for Ethiopian relief even a frugal man like my husband wrote out a hundred-dollar check, *she* was on that plane. *She* was going to spend July and August with grandparents because Pam wouldn't go. Pam said she'd rather waitress at McDonald's. 'If it's a choice between Bombay and Wonderland, I'm picking Wonderland,' she'd said.

'Leave me alone,' Kusum yells. 'You know what I want to do? If I didn't have to look after you now, I'd hang myself.'

Pam's young face goes blotchy with pain. 'Thanks,' she says, 'don't let me stop you.'

'Hush,' pregnant Mrs Sharma scolds Pam. 'Leave your mother alone. Mr Sharma will tackle the reporters and fill out the forms. He'll say what has to be said.'

Pam stands her ground. 'You think I don't know what Mummy's thinking? *Why her?* that's what. That's sick! Mummy wishes my little sister were alive and I were dead.'

Kusum's hand in mine is trembly hot. We continue to sit on the stairs.

She calls before she arrives, wondering if there's anything I need. Her name is Judith Templeton and she's an appointee of the provincial government. 'Multiculturalism?' I ask, and she says, 'partially,' but that her mandate is bigger. 'I've been told you knew many of the people on the flight,' she says. 'Perhaps if you'd agree to help us reach the others . . . ?'

She gives me time at least to put on tea water and pick up the mess in the front room. I have a few samosas from Kusum's housewarming that I could fry up, but then I think, why prolong this visit?

Judith Templeton is much younger than she sounded. She wears a blue suit with a white blouse and a polkadot tie. Her blonde hair is cut short, her only jewelry is pearl drop earrings. Her briefcase is new and expensive looking, a gleaming cordovan leather. She sits with it across her lap. When she looks out the front windows onto the street, her contact lenses seem to float in front of her light blue eyes.

'What sort of help do you want from me?' I ask. She has refused the tea, out of politeness, but I insist, along with some slightly stale biscuits.

'I have no experience,' she admits. 'That is, I have an MSW and I've worked in liaison with accident victims, but I mean I have no experience with a tragedy of this scale – '

'Who could?' I ask.

' – and with the complications of culture, language, and customs. Someone mentioned that Mrs Bhave is a pillar – because you've taken it more calmly.'

At this, perhaps, I frown, for she reaches forward, almost to take my hand. 'I hope you understand my meaning, Mrs Bhave. There are hundreds of people in Metro directly affected, like you, and some of them speak no English. There are some widows who've never handled money or gone on a bus, and there are old parents who still haven't eaten or gone outside their bedrooms. Some houses and apartments have been looted. Some wives are still hysterical. Some husbands are in shock and profound depression. We want to help, but our hands are tied in so many ways. We have to distribute money to some people, and there are legal documents – these things can be done. We have interpreters, but we don't always have the human touch, or maybe the right human touch. We don't want to make mistakes, Mrs Bhave, and that's why we'd like to ask you to help us.'

'More mistakes, you mean,' I say.

'Police matters are not in my hands,' she answers.

'Nothing I can do will make any difference,' I say. 'We must all grieve in our own way.'

'But you are coping very well. All the people said, Mrs Bhave is the strongest person of all. Perhaps if the others could see you, talk with you, it would help them.'

'By the standards of the people you call hysterical, I am behaving very oddly and very badly, Miss Templeton.' I want to say to her, *I wish I could scream, starve, walk into Lake Ontario, jump from a bridge*. 'They would not see me as a model. I do not see myself as a model.'

I am a freak. No one who has ever known me would think of me reacting this way. This terrible calm will not go away.

She asks me if she may call again, after I get back from a long trip that we all must make. 'Of course,' I say. 'Feel free to call, anytime.'

*

Four days later, I find Kusum squatting on a rock overlooking a bay in Ireland. It isn't a big rock, but it juts sharply out over water. This is as close as we'll ever get to them. June breezes balloon out her sari and unpin her knee-length hair. She has the bewildered look of a sea creature whom the tides have stranded.

It's been one hundred hours since Kusum came stumbling and screaming across my lawn. Waiting around the hospital, we've heard many stories. The police, the diplomats, they tell us things thinking that we're strong, that knowledge is helpful to the grieving, and maybe it is. Some, I know, prefer ignorance, or their own versions. The plane broke into two, they say. Unconsciousness was instantaneous. No one suffered. My boys must have just finished their breakfasts. They loved eating on planes, they loved the smallness of plates, knives, and forks. Last year they saved the airline salt and pepper shakers. Half an hour more and they would have made it to Heathrow.

Kusum says that we can't escape our fate. She says that all those people – our husbands, my boys, her girl with the nightingale voice, all those Hindus, Christians, Sikhs, Muslims, Parsis, and atheists on that plane – were fated to die together off this beautiful bay. She learned this from a swami in Toronto.

I have my Valium.

Six of us 'relatives' – two widows and four widowers – choose to spend the day today by the waters instead of sitting in a hospital room and scanning photographs of the dead. That's what they call us now: relatives. I've looked through twenty-seven photos in two days. They're very kind to us, the Irish are very understanding. Sometimes understanding means freeing a tourist bus for this trip to the bay, so we can pretend to spy our loved ones through the glassiness of waves or in sun-speckled cloud shapes.

I could die here, too, and be content.

'What is that, out there?' She's standing and flapping her hands and for a moment I see a head shape bobbing in the waves.

She's standing in the water, I, on the boulder. The tide is low, and a round, black, head-sized rock has just risen from the waves. She returns, her sari end dripping and ruined and her face is a twisted remnant of hope, the way mine was a hundred hours ago, still laughing but inwardly knowing that nothing but the ultimate tragedy could bring two women together at six o'clock on a Sunday morning. I watch her face sag into blankness.

'That water felt warm, Shaila,' she says at length.

'You can't,' I say. 'We have to wait for our turn to come.'

I haven't eaten in four days, haven't brushed my teeth.

'I know,' she says. 'I tell myself I have no right to grieve. They are in a better place than we are. My swami says I should be thrilled for them. My swami says depression is a sign of our selfishness.'

Maybe I'm selfish. Selfishly I break away from Kusum and run, sandals slapping against stones, to the water's edge. What if my boys aren't lying pinned under the debris? What if they aren't stuck a mile below that innocent blue chop? What if, given the strong currents . . .

Now I've ruined my sari, one of my best. Kusum has joined me, knee-deep in water that feels to me like a swimming pool. I could settle in the water, and my husband would take my hand and the boys would slap water in my face just to see me scream.

'Do you remember what good swimmers my boys were, Kusum?'

'I saw the medals,' she says.

One of the widowers, Dr Ranganathan from Montreal, walks out to us, carrying his shoes in one hand. He's an electrical engineer. Someone at the hotel mentioned his work is famous around the world, something about the place where physics and electricity come together. He has lost a huge family, something indescribable. 'With some luck,' Dr Ranganathan suggests to me, 'a good swimmer could make it safely to some island. It is quite possible that there may be many, many microscopic islets scattered around.'

'You're not just saying that?' I tell Dr Ranganathan about Vinod, my elder son. Last year he took diving as well.

'It's a parent's duty to hope,' he says. 'It is foolish to rule out possibilities that have not been tested. I myself have not surrendered hope.'

Kusum is sobbing once again. 'Dear lady,' he says, laying his free hand on her arm, and she calms down.

'Vinod is how old?' he asks me. He's very careful, as we all are. *Is*, not was.

'Fourteen. Yesterday he was fourteen. His father and uncle were going to take him down to the Taj and give him a big birthday party. I couldn't go with them because I couldn't get two weeks off from my stupid job in June.' I process bills for a travel agent. June is a big travel month.

Dr Ranganathan whips the pockets of his suit jacket inside out. Squashed roses, in darkening shades of pink, float on the water. He tore the roses off creepers in somebody's garden. He didn't ask anyone if he could pluck the roses, but now there's been an article about it in the local papers. When you see an Indian person, it says, please give him or her flowers.

'A strong youth of fourteen,' he says, 'can very likely pull to safety a younger one.'

My sons, though four years apart, were very close. Vinod wouldn't let Mithun drown. *Electrical engineering*, I think, foolishly perhaps: this man knows important secrets of the universe, things closed to me. Relief spins me lightheaded. No wonder my boys' photographs haven't turned up in the gallery of photos of the recovered dead. 'Such pretty roses,' I say.

'My wife loved pink roses. Every Friday I had to bring a bunch home. I used to say, why? After twenty-odd years of marriage you're still needing proof positive of my love?' He has identified his wife and three of his children. Then others from Montreal, the lucky ones, intact families with no survivors. He chuckles as he wades back to shore. Then he swings around to ask me a question. 'Mrs Bhave, you are wanting to throw in some roses for your loved ones? I have two big ones left.'

But I have other things to float: Vinod's pocket calculator; a half-painted model B-52 for my Mithun. They'd want them on their island. And for my husband? For him I let fall into the calm, glassy waters a poem I wrote in the hospital yesterday. Finally he'll know my feelings for him.

'Don't tumble, the rocks are slippery,' Dr Ranganathan cautions. He holds out a hand for me to grab.

Then it's time to get back on the bus, time to rush back to our waiting posts on hospital benches.

Kusum is one of the lucky ones. The lucky ones flew here, identified in multiplicate their loved ones, then will fly to India with the bodies for proper ceremonies. Satish is one of the few males who surfaced. The photos of faces we saw on the walls in an office at Heathrow and here in the hospital are mostly of women. Women have more body fat, a nun said to me matter-of-factly. They float better.

Today I was stopped by a young sailor on the street. He had loaded bodies, he'd gone into the water when – he checks my face for signs of strength – when the sharks were first spotted. I don't blush, and he breaks down. 'It's all right,' I say. 'Thank you.' I had heard about the sharks from Dr Ranganathan. In his orderly mind, science brings understanding, it holds no terror. It is the shark's duty. For every deer there is a hunter, for every fish a fisherman.

The Irish are not shy; they rush to me and give me hugs and some are crying. I cannot imagine reactions like that on the streets of Toronto. Just strangers, and I am touched. Some carry flowers with them and give them to any Indian they see.

After lunch, a policeman I have gotten to know quite well catches hold of me. He says he thinks he has a match for Vinod. I explain what a good swimmer Vinod is.

'You want me with you when you look at photos?' Dr Ranganathan walks ahead of me into the picture gallery. In these matters, he is a scientist, and I am grateful. It is a new perspective. 'They have performed miracles,' he says. 'We are indebted to them.'

The first day or two the policemen showed us relatives only one picture at a time; now they're in a hurry, they're eager to lay out the possibles, and even the probables.

The face on the photo is of a boy much like Vinod; the same intelligent eyes, the same thick brows dipping into a V. But this boy's features, even his cheeks, are puffier, wider, mushier.

'No.' My gaze is pulled by other pictures. There are five other boys who look like Vinod.

The nun assigned to console me rubs the first picture with a fingertip. 'When they've been in the water for a while, love, they look a little heavier.' The bones under the skin are broken, they said on the first day – try to adjust your memories. It's important.

'It's not him. I'm his mother. I'd know.'

'I know this one!' Dr Ranganathan cries out suddenly from the back of the gallery. 'And this one!' I think he senses that I don't want to find my boys. 'They are the Kutty brothers. They were also from Montreal.' I don't mean to be crying. On the contrary, I am ecstatic. My suitcase in the hotel is packed heavy with dry clothes for my boys.

The policeman starts to cry. 'I am so sorry, I am so sorry, ma'am. I really thought we had a match.'

With the nun ahead of us and the policeman behind, we, the unlucky ones without our children's bodies, file out of the makeshift gallery.

From Ireland most of us go on to India. Kusum and I take the same direct flight to Bombay, so I can help her clear customs quickly. But we have to argue with a man in uniform. He has large boils on his face. The boils swell and glow with sweat as we argue with him. He wants Kusum to wait in line and he refuses to take authority because his boss is on a tea break. But Kusum won't let her coffins out of sight, and I shan't desert her though I know that my parents, elderly and diabetic, must be waiting in a stuffy car in a scorching lot.

'You bastard!' I scream at the man with the popping boils. Other passengers press closer. 'You think we're smuggling contraband in those coffins!'

Once upon a time we were well brought up women; we were dutiful wives who kept our heads veiled, our voices shy and sweet.

In India, I become, once again, an only child of rich, ailing parents. Old friends of the family come to pay their respects. Some are Sikh, and inwardly, involuntarily, I cringe. My parents are progressive people; they do not blame communities for a few individuals.

In Canada it is a different story now.

'Stay longer,' my mother pleads. 'Canada is a cold place. Why would you want to be all by yourself?' I stay.

Three months pass. Then another.

'Vikram wouldn't have wanted you to give up things!' they protest. They call my husband by the name he was born with. In Toronto he'd changed to Vik so the men he worked with at his office would find his name as easy as Rod or Chris. 'You know, the dead aren't cut off from us!'

My grandmother, the spoiled daughter of a rich *zamindar*, shaved her head with rusty razor blades when she was widowed at sixteen. My grandfather died of childhood diabetes when he was nineteen, and she saw herself as the harbinger of bad luck. My mother grew up without parents, raised indifferently by an uncle, while her true mother slept in a hut behind the main estate house and took her food with the servants. She grew up a rationalist. My parents abhor mindless mortification.

The *zamindar*'s daughter kept stubborn faith in Vedic rituals; my parents rebelled. I am trapped between two modes of knowledge. At thirty-six, I am too old to start over and too young to give up. Like my husband's spirit, I flutter between worlds.

*

Courting aphasia, we travel. We travel with our phalanx of servants and poor relatives. To hill stations and to beach resorts. We play contract bridge in dusty gymkhana clubs. We ride stubby ponies up crumbly mountain trails. At tea dances, we let ourselves be twirled twice round the ballroom. We hit the holy spots we hadn't made time for before. In Varanasi, Kalighat, Rishikesh, Hardwar, astrologers and palmists seek me out and for a fee offer me cosmic consolations.

Already the widowers among us are being shown new bride candidates. They cannot resist the call of custom, the authority of their parents and older brothers. They must marry; it is the duty of a man to look after a wife. The new wives will be young widows with children, destitute but of good family. They will make loving wives, but the men will shun them. I've had calls from the men over crackling Indian telephone lines. 'Save me,' they say, these substantial, educated, successful men of forty. 'My parents are arranging a marriage for me.' In a month they will have buried one family and returned to Canada with a new bride and partial family.

I am comparatively lucky. No one here thinks of arranging a husband for an unlucky widow.

Then, on the third day of the sixth month into this odyssey, in an abandoned temple in a tiny Himalayan village, as I make my offering of flowers and sweetmeats to the god of a tribe of animists, my husband descends to me. He is squatting next to a scrawny *sadhu* in moth-eaten robes. Vikram wears the vanilla suit he wore the last time I hugged him. The *sadhu* tosses petals on a butter-fed flame, reciting Sanskrit mantras and sweeps his face of flies. My husband takes my hands in his.

You're beautiful, he starts. Then, *What are you doing here?*

Shall I stay? I ask. He only smiles, but already the image is fading. *You must finish alone what we started together.* No seaweed wreathes his mouth. He speaks too fast just as he used to when we were an envied family in our pink split-level. He is gone.

In the windowless altar room, smoky with joss sticks and clarified butter lamps, a sweaty hand gropes for my blouse. I do not shriek. The *sadhu* arranges his robe. The lamps hiss and sputter out.

When we come out of the temple, my mother says, 'Did you feel something weird in there?'

My mother has no patience with ghosts, prophetic dreams, holy men, and cults.

'No,' I lie. 'Nothing.'

But she knows that she's lost me. She knows that in days I shall be leaving.

Kusum's put her house up for sale. She wants to live in an ashram in Hardwar. Moving to Hardwar was her swami's idea. Her swami runs two ashrams, the one in Hardwar and another here in Toronto.

'Don't run away,' I tell her.

'I'm not running away,' she says. 'I'm pursuing inner peace. You think you or that Ranganathan fellow are better off?'

Pam's left for California. She wants to do some modelling, she says. She says when she comes into her share of the insurance money she'll open a yoga-cum-aerobics studio in Hollywood. She sends me postcards so naughty I daren't leave them on the coffee table. Her mother has withdrawn from her and the world.

The rest of us don't lose touch, that's the point. Talk is all we have, says Dr Ranganathan, who has also resisted his relatives and returned to Montreal and to his job, alone. He says, whom better to talk with than other relatives? We've been melted down and recast as a new tribe.

He calls me twice a week from Montreal. Every Wednesday night and every Saturday afternoon. He is changing jobs, going to Ottawa. But Ottawa is over a hundred miles away, and he is forced to drive two hundred and twenty miles a day. He can't bring himself to sell his house. The house is a temple, he says; the king-sized bed in the master bedroom is a shrine. He sleeps on a folding cot. A devotee.

*

There are still some hysterical relatives. Judith Templeton's list of those needing help and those who've 'accepted' is in nearly perfect balance. Acceptance means you speak of your family in the past tense and you make active plans for moving ahead with your life. There are courses at Seneca and Ryerson we could be taking. Her gleaming leather briefcase is full of college catalogues and lists of cultural societies that need our help. She has done impressive work, I tell her.

'In the textbooks on grief management,' she replies – I am her confidante, I realise, one of the few whose grief has not sprung bizarre obsessions – 'there are stages to pass through: rejection, depression, acceptance, reconstruction.' She has compiled a chart and finds that six months after the tragedy, none of us still reject reality, but only a handful are reconstructing. 'Depressed acceptance' is the plateau we've reached. Remarriage is a major step in reconstruction (though she's a little surprised, even shocked, over *how* quickly some of the men have taken on new families). Selling one's house and changing jobs and cities is healthy.

How do I tell Judith Templeton that my family surrounds me, and that like creatures in epics, they've changed shapes? She sees me as calm and accepting but worries that I have no job, no career. My closest friends are worse off than I. I cannot tell her my days, even my nights, are thrilling.

She asks me to help with families she can't reach at all. An elderly couple in Agincourt whose sons were killed just weeks after they had brought their parents over from a village in Punjab. From their names, I know they are Sikh. Judith Templeton and a translator have visited them twice with offers of money for air fares to Ireland, with bank forms, power-of-attorney forms, but they have refused to sign, or to leave their tiny apartment. Their sons' money is frozen in the bank. Their sons' investment apartments have been trashed by tenants, the furnishings sold off. The parents fear that anything they sign or any money they receive will end the company's or the country's obligations to them. They fear they are selling their sons for two airline tickets to a place they've never seen.

The high-rise apartment is a tower of Indians and West Indians, with a sprinkling of Orientals. The nearest bus stop kiosk is lined with women in saris. Boys practice cricket in the parking lot. Inside the building, even I wince a bit from the ferocity of onion fumes, the distinctive and immediate Indianness of frying *ghee*, but Judith Templeton maintains a steady flow of information. These poor old people are in imminent danger of losing their place and all their services.

I say to her, 'They are Sikh. They will not open up to a Hindu woman.' And what I want to add is, as much as I try not to, I stiffen now at the sight of beards and turbans. I remember a time when we all trusted each other in this new country, it was only the new country we worried about.

The two rooms are dark and stuffy. The lights are off, and an oil lamp sputters on the coffee table. The bent old lady has let us in, and her husband is wrapping a white turban over his oiled, hip-length hair. She immediately goes to the kitchen, and I hear the most familiar sound of an Indian home, tap water hitting and filling a teapot.

They have not paid their utility bills, out of fear and the inability to write a check. The telephone is gone; electricity and gas and water are soon to follow. They have told Judith their sons will provide. They are good boys, and they have always earned and looked after their parents.

We converse a bit in Hindi. They do not ask about the crash and I wonder if I should bring it up. If they think I am here merely as a translator, then they may feel insulted. There are thousands of Punjabi-speakers, Sikhs, in Toronto to do a better job. And so I say to the old lady, 'I too have lost my sons, and my husband, in the crash.'

Her eyes immediately fill with tears. The man mutters a few words which sound like a blessing. 'God provides and God takes away,' he says.

I want to say, but only men destroy and give back nothing.

'My boys and my husband are not coming back,' I say. 'We have to understand that.'

Now the old woman responds. 'But who is to say? Man alone does not decide these things.' To this her husband adds his agreement.

Judith asks about the bank papers, the release forms. With a stroke of the pen, they will have a provincial trustee to pay their bills, invest their money, send them a monthly pension.

'Do you know this woman?' I ask them.

The man raises his hand from the table, turns it over and seems to regard each finger separately before he answers. 'This young lady is always coming here, we make tea for her and she leaves papers for us to sign.' His eyes scan a pile of papers in the corner of the room. 'Soon we will be out of tea, then will she go away?'

The old lady adds, 'I have asked my neighbors and no one else gets *angrezi* visitors. What have we done?'

'It's her job,' I try to explain. 'The government is worried. Soon you will have no place to stay, no lights, no gas, no water.'

'Government will get its money. Tell her not to worry, we are honorable people.'

I try to explain the government wishes to give money, not take. He raises his hand. 'Let them take,' he says. 'We are accustomed to that. That is no problem.'

'We are strong people,' says the wife. 'Tell her that.'

'Who needs all this machinery?' demands the husband. 'It is unhealthy, the bright lights, the cold air on a hot day, the cold food, the four gas rings. God will provide, not government.'

'When our boys return,' the mother says. Her husband sucks his teeth. 'Enough talk,' he says.

Judith breaks in. 'Have you convinced them?' The snaps on her cordovan briefcase go off like firecrackers in that quiet apartment. She lays the sheaf of legal papers on the coffee table. 'If they can't write their names, an X will do – I've told them that.'

Now the old lady has shuffled to the kitchen and soon

emerges with a pot of tea and two cups. 'I think my bladder will go first on a job like this,' Judith says to me, smiling. 'If only there was some way of reaching them. Please thank her for the tea. Tell her she's very kind.'

I nod in Judith's direction and tell them in Hindi, 'She thanks you for the tea. She thinks you are being very hospitable but she doesn't have the slightest idea what it means.'

I want to say, humor her. I want to say, my boys and my husband are with me too, more than ever. I look in the old man's eyes and I can read his stubborn, peasant's message: *I have protected this woman as best I can. She is the only person I have left. Give to me or take from me what you will, but I will not sign for it. I will not pretend that I accept.*

In the car, Judith says, 'You see what I'm up against? I'm sure they're lovely people, but their stubbornness and ignorance are driving me crazy. They think signing a paper is signing their sons' death warrants, don't they?'

I am looking out the window. I want to say, *In our culture, it is a parent's duty to hope.*

'Now Shaila, this next woman is a real mess. She cries day and night, and she refuses all medical help. We may have to – '

' – Let me out at the subway,' I say.

'I beg your pardon?' I can feel those blue eyes staring at me.

It would not be like her to disobey. She merely disapproves, and slows at a corner to let me out. Her voice is plaintive. 'Is there anything I said? Anything I did?'

I could answer her suddenly in a dozen ways, but I choose not to. 'Shaila? Let's talk about it,' I hear, then slam the door.

A wife and mother begins her new life in a new country, and that life is cut short. Yet her husband tells her: complete what we have started. We, who stayed out of politics and came halfway around the world to avoid religious and political feuding have been the first in the New World to die from it. I no longer know what we started, nor how to complete it.

I write letters to the editors of local papers and to members of Parliament. Now at least they admit it was a bomb. One MP answers back, with sympathy, but with a challenge. You want to make a difference? Work on a campaign. Work on mine. Politicise the Indian voter.

My husband's old lawyer helps me set up a trust. Vikram was a saver and a careful investor. He had saved the boys' boarding-school and college fees. I sell the pink house at four times what we paid for it and take a small apartment downtown. I am looking for a charity to support.

We are deep in the Toronto winter, gray skies, icy pavements. I stay indoors, watching television. I have tried to assess my situation, how best to live my life, to complete what we began so many years ago. Kusum has written me from Hardwar that her life is now serene. She has seen Satish and has heard her daughter sing again. Kusum was on a pilgrimage, passing through a village when she heard a young girl's voice, singing one of her daughter's favorite *bhajans*. She followed the music through the squalor of a Himalayan village, to a hut where a young girl, an exact replica of her daughter, was fanning coals under the kitchen fire. When she appeared, the girl cried out, 'Ma!' and ran away. What did I think of that?

I think I can only envy her.

Pam didn't make it to California, but writes me from Vancouver. She works in a department store, giving make-up hints to Indian and Oriental girls. Dr Ranganathan has given up his commute, given up his house and job, and accepted an academic position in Texas where no one knows his story and he has vowed not to tell it. He calls me now once a week.

I wait, I listen, and I pray, but Vikram has not returned to me. The voices and the shapes and the nights filled with visions ended abruptly several weeks ago.

I take it as a sign.

One rare, beautiful, sunny day last week, returning from a small errand on Yonge Street, I was walking through the park from the subway to my apartment. I live equidistant from the

Ontario Houses of Parliament and the University of Toronto. The day was not cold, but something in the bare trees caught my attention. I looked up from the gravel, into the branches and the clear blue sky beyond. I thought I heard the rustling of larger forms, and I waited a moment for voices. Nothing.

'What?' I asked.

Then as I stood in the path looking north to Queen's Park and west to the university, I heard the voices of my family one last time. *Your time has come*, they said. *Go, be brave*.

I do not know where this voyage I have begun will end. I do not know which direction I will take. I dropped the package on a park bench and started walking.

The Listeners

Yasmin Issacs

Congregated
their chatter
fills the room
heavy with uncertainties
watching
they listen from afar

feel
disquiet of their hearts
echoing
pensive tones
sending chills
through their bones

Outbursts
shrill to stillness
greeting watered eyes

Women
sharing memories
sharing hardship
sharing pain
of the day they came

heart rending
belly pain
sucklings
pulled from breasts

The children
the listeners
move
uneasy on the periphery
drawn
to the intensity
of their poignancy.
Needing
to know
they listened.
Talked of the madness
besetting them day and night
neither eat nor sleep
mourning the children
they left behind.

Breasts
milk filled/dripping
empty arms/aching

Gloom fills the room
silent
sobs turn to wails
shuddering
pain touching pain

There were tales of children
of regret
of a mother's pain

Hot
airless room

silent
swaying
bubbling

Erupt

Spewing rage
from deep within

Never been told
their grief
their loss
for the children
the listeners.

Erratum

Michael Donoghy

I touch the cold flesh of a god in the V and A,
the guard asleep in his chair, and I'm shocked
to find it's plaster. These are the reproduction rooms,
where the David stands side by side with the Moses
and Trajan's column (in two halves).
It reminds me of the inventory sequence in *Citizen Kane*.
It reminds me of an evening twenty years ago.

And all at once I'm there, at her side,
turning the pages as she plays
from the yellowed song sheets I rescued from a bookstall:
Dodd's setting of *Antony and Cleopatra*. All very improving.
'Give me my robe and crown,' she warbles
in a Victorian coloratura. 'I have immoral longings in me.'

I want to correct her – the word on the page is
immortal – but I'm fourteen and scandalised.
(I knew there were no innocent mistakes.
I'd finished *Modern Masters: Freud*
before she snatched and burned it. 'Filth' –
yanking each signature free of the spine,
'Filth. Filth. Filth.')

The song is over. But when she smiles at me,
I'm on the verge of tears, staring down at the gap-
toothed grimace of our old Bechstein. 'What's wrong?'
'What's *wrong*? I check the word again. She's right. Immoral.
She shows me the printer's slip, infecting
the back page of every copy, like,
she might have said, the first sin.

The guard snorts in his dream. I take my palm away
still cool from what I'd taken to be marble.
And when I get that moment back, it's later;
I'm sobbing on her shoulder and I can't say why.
So she suggests another visit to the furnace, where,
to comfort me, perhaps, we rake the cinders with the music
till they chink and spark, and shove the pages
straight to the white core to watch them darken as if ageing,
blacken, enfold, like a sped-up film of blossoms in reverse.

Painting on Glass

Aamer Hussein

Last night: I went to see a Malay film at the South Bank I had been asked to review. The blurb for it had announced serious themes, fundamentalism and feminism and polygyny and Palestinian refugees, but what we saw was a work full of vitality, of romance and butterflies and reconciliations. I struggled with cynicism and suspended it, thinking of the challenge and the problems of presenting a message to a mass audience in a 'developing' country, of addressing issues and causes in a coherent voice, treading the tightrope between the aesthetic and the popular and paying homage to both . . . but each clumsy cut, each musical interlude and sentimental gesture was greeted with a chorus of catcalls and guffaws by an audience that didn't know when to laugh and when to cry.

As I left the theatre and walked towards the bridge that leads to Embankment station I jingled the coins in my pocket, ready for the hungry hands and eyes of the homeless that haunt the narrow path. At least I'd buy a *Big Issue* for the tube ride home. There but for fortune, I often think. It was raining, an untimely grey early June drizzle. The surging sound of a saxophone stopped me and I turned to look: a woman was dancing to the music of a cassette recorder, dancing with her eyes closed and tossing a red rag from her hand up into the air like a weightless partner, dancing ecstatic and shockingly alone. I don't know what her dancing did to me, but suddenly I wanted to be by myself. I wanted to be at home, and I ran. It wasn't even dark yet but the clouds had swallowed the sunset for supper and the river was the colour of dishwater.

I don't know why I'm writing all this but since Tahira left for Karachi I've been going a lot to the cinema on my own and thinking of the films and the music she liked. And of the story she'd asked me to write about my life and send to Pakistan for her to publish in her journal; everything I see and hear seems to flow into it. I wanted to write something spare and stark and simple because over the last few years I've always thought that simplicity speaks to the widest possible audience, but the film I'd seen made me think again. I wondered what Tahira would have said about it, what she'd have said to the woman who'd directed it, how they'd have talked about Islam, censorship, roots and social responsibility. I thought about the films made by Asians here, those tales of estrangement and compromise, *Samosas on the Sand* and *Tennessee Tandoori* and *Croydon Country Singers* and *The Krishna of the Counties*, how I'd colluded in her mocking comments about them until I realised that she saw me, too, as an alienated migrant cut off from my roots, and I knew that she was waiting for me to prove myself with something new, something authentic. I begin to think about the heaviness of trees: in our country, in our verses, we talk about the displaced as birds without wings, birds who can no longer fly to their destination, and words about roots and sources began to disturb me. Because trees have heavy bodies; a tree removed from its native soil and planted elsewhere puts down new roots, twisted ones, perhaps, but its trunk grows heavy. You try to leave and something pulls at you, the earth holds you back. The soil of a new language and new necessities. I thought of the day I'd walked down Guildford Street on my way to Russell Square and seen a dead rat thrown out on the pavement, and that evening a pigeon, mangled, red and crushed, lay on what I could swear was the very same spot. I began to wish I could find my lost sky, my horizon, my lost words. Films and television have taken over from painters and poets, and we're all left stranded with dead images like piles of dead leaves, dead butterflies, dead birds. Robbed of their source in a living language. I've always held that art should be both beautiful and useful, but when in doubt I've usually thrown the beauty out. Though perhaps the way to reach people is to talk in those primary colours that this wretched drizzle seems to wash away, to fill stories with light and animation and so what if the audience laughs at the tragic moments: let the emotions spill over the top, and maybe the happy scenes and gestures will make them cry. Simplicity rests in the pact – I've been there, I know – between the teller and listener, not in sentence structures or narrative lines. People recognise and relate to complications and clutter – after all, they're what make up our lives. It's the content that matters, in the end. Perhaps it's innocence we laugh at, the innocence of belief, but we long for it too, the mess and the muddle and the ache of betrayal.

Enough rambling, enough reflection. Let's get on with it, let me tell you about my life. My name is Irfan Malik. I've been in London eight years. I was born in Pakistan thirty-six years ago and grew up in Lahore. I took a couple of degrees there and after doing a stint at an advertising agency I went into journalism, working for television and co-editing a popular fortnightly English review. I also wrote poetry and TV plays in Urdu and Punjabi and published a book about the things I saw and I knew, about my grandparents' village and about the city and love and corruption and change, the usual bourgeois stuff, you could say, but it was what I loved doing and it brought me some applause, and also some censure from my politically correct mates but even they said I had a flair for words and images.

I don't really suppose that I was a great success as a Pakistani man – poetry and such are hardly the material middle-class parents' dreams are made of – but I'm a second son and it didn't really matter. My elder brother went abroad to study medicine and my parents couldn't afford to send me overseas, anyway. I made some kind of independent living. But when my chance came I took it, and you could say my chance was engineered by my parents. And Aneela's. She was the daughter of distant relatives. Attractive, brilliantly well educated by anyone's standards, she came to Lahore on what we used to call a shopping trip at college and chose me as the asset she was shopping for. She was on the rebound; her long relationship with an Americanised Pakistani had broken, I was a relative of respectable origins, and she said she loved my love poems – I wrote one about our second meeting which was, well, intense. She was an odd mixture of chic and sluttish and that seemed sophisticated and ineffably foreign to me. Her father had a newspaper chain in London as a tax outlet and they'd opened an English section, a serious political and cultural review. I would be perfect as its acting editor: I had the experience and the talent.

So it was London for me. An approved rather than an arranged marriage. The in-laws' house in Bramham Gardens – which they insisted was in South Ken, though it's actually Earls Court – and the office and my book of verse published in Lahore clutched under my arm and Third World poetry readings which my journal's budget occasionally allowed me to organise. I met poets from Africa and Latin America and the Arab world and sometimes they invited me to read with them. London was still political in those days, at least in its Third World peripheries, and Marxism hadn't yet become a bad smell. I knew my poems occasionally aroused a frown or worse still a sneer, which was strange, because it made me realise that though I hadn't been particularly aware of it I'd been speaking to an international audience all the time, and international meant English-speaking. No one was desperate to translate my work so I found myself dealing, to what I now see as my detriment, with a new language. I'd somehow mixed up the translations of Neruda and Paz I'd read with English poetry, which I knew almost nothing about, but that, that was another world altogether, and the dark-skinned poets I met here in our segregated enclaves were angry.

Really angry. About imperalism and exploitation and racism. I learned their language: I began to write protest poetry too. After all, I was, by their admission, a man of the Third World, and I came from a country in the metal grasp of a military apparatus. Once an English patron of writers of colour, slightly the worse for drink, accused me of being, as a Pakistani, a partisan of oppression and Islam and misogyny because I made the mistake of telling her to accept an invitation to speak about her writing in a British Council tour of Pakistan. Those were the days of the Rushdie affair and it wasn't exactly chic to be Pakistani or Muslim. I responded for once in that angry manner with which I was becoming familiar. And what about your fucking Tories, I said. They've got you all by the balls and none of you even admits that there are beggars and homeless around everywhere on your streets. I had my material – you only had to read an article about Pakistan or watch a documentary to get it – and I had apartheid, intifada, Ethiopia, Timor and Tiananmen to supplement that. We carry our histories on our backs, I wrote, in our blood and in our bones. But at the same time I knew somewhere in these bones of mine that what we were doing was only ranting and raving and preaching to each other and to the ranks of the already rallied, our words wouldn't get us to where we really wanted to go, our well of words was running out of fresh water as if a cow or worse still a pig had died in it. That we didn't have the courage to face an era which had placed us in a safe asylum, where we could scream the screams of dumb bright birds just as long as we didn't make a noise in the neighbourhood, disturb the local residents by shattering the glass walls of our aviary.

And then, four years after I came here, things fell apart.

My father-in-law was accused – rightly or wrongly – of malpractices in his business dealings and had to run. His empire was frozen and the newspaper chain bought out. Looking back at that time I wonder if I put it into words then what I know now: we'd never really belonged as an elite, we'd only lived here in a replica of our ways at home or as a distorted reflection of the West's well-off. As long as they could bear us in their midst. But at some time, as the tide of financial return went down lower and lower our status as a class within a class had to change, too. Someone brought down an axe to break our mirror and it's no use, citing conspiracy theories and Western fears of Third World gain and prosperity to explain our downfall by degrees.

My marriage had frozen, too, in its second year, and though we remained quite civilised with each other and still slept together desultorily Aneela and I led our own lives. Aneela hadn't ever got over her great love and her vodka drinking became hazardous. Most of the time she was a good enough mother to our little daughter and it was Suhayla that kept us together – still does, in a way. It was understood before I moved myself and my abilities to London that I'd be improving my educational qualifications here. And my abilities, it emerged, were negligible in Aneela's eyes, since she'd never managed to mould me into the model of moneyed manhood she'd imagined. My decision to take a degree in history rather than the MBA she was insisting I should do made me look to her even more like the under-achieving wimp she already thought I was. I got my Master's from evening classes at Birkbeck. She'd thought it would be better to do a course in journalism, at least, and maybe she was right; I realised that when I found myself a sojourner on the swelling tide of unemployment. When I couldn't find anything else someone suggested I take a course in English as a Second Language which the redundancy money that had somehow come my way from the liquidators helped to fund. So there I was, at thirty-two, with a bagful of qualifications none of which amounted to very much, and I'd realised long ago that I certainly wasn't the poet of the age. I knew, though, that I wasn't bad either: that was proved when a Caribbean publisher as well respected for his radical politics as for his generous and tough aesthetic commissioned a collection of my London work. He brought out a slim volume called *After the Death of Zia, Thatcher and Reagan* a year after Aneela left for Boston, her lover and yet another redundant degree. She's never done a thing with her hopes or her high educational achievements.

I was a grass widower. Aneela hadn't talked about divorce, maybe for Suhayla's sake. We clung together for a bit like rain-drenched children and seemed to be sexually alive to each other like we'd been before. Then one night I heard her telling her best friend on the phone how her lover had rung her up for a drink while he was passing through town and she couldn't resist seeing him, telling herself it was only a greeting for the sake of the past, then in the deserted hotel bar late that winter night he'd touched her as if they were in bed again, she'd found herself half-undressed right there on the sofa and when she told him to stop he left her there, like that, humiliated but alive again or half-alive, because the part of her that he'd left behind was dead, had been dead for so long, and the part of herself she'd shared with me was dying now. I never told her that I'd heard but she knew that I knew it was really over. She said when she left that she only wanted to clear her head and I pretended I believed she'd be back soon. Suhayla cried a lot when we said goodbye but I let her go because I knew that with the life ahead of me I couldn't afford to look after her or give her the things she was used to. Soon after they went I moved from Earls Court to a short life flat in EC1 a classmate from my ESL group was vacating to move to Australia: bedsit and attached bath and no cooking facilities, only a single ring on which I could boil water for tea or an egg and use as a heater when it got too cold. I could barely afford even that. I came to know every chip shop in the area and when the grungy walls sang dirges to me I sat for hours with elbows on sticky white tables over a paper glass of Coke at Burger King with strobe lights in my eyes.

When I felt really hollow those things about Aneela that I'd taken for granted, those cheating memories, perhaps, from which we sketch our similes, trickled down my face like sweat in the hot lights: the feeling of her nipples and the underslopes of her breasts beneath my fingers and how her back warmed against me as she fell asleep, the thought of her hands and how, when I turned away from her in sleepy forgetfulness, she'd run her fingers down from the bones above my chest to my sex and back up again until every bit of me, even the hairs on my body, woke up. You remember those things more vividly than lovemaking when you lose them.

Going back to Lahore was out and I never even considered it. My doctor father had retired years ago and moved to Rawalpindi to be close to my brother and his family who'd settled in Islamabad, which was strange to me. I'd only visited them there a couple of times since my marriage. I suppose I understand now why I didn't leave London: damaged goods can be returned to their sellers and their makers, but what about goods that are damaged on the way, or broken by their buyers? Who'll want to have those back? I think that's how I felt. Why the hell should Pakistan want me, the mediocre editor of a small-circulation Third World journal, a little-known poet who'd long ago lost touch with home; with a degree in history which wasn't even a doctorate? What would I do there – teach English as a second language to the children of the rich who'd grown up speaking English anyway? Anyone who left a home will know what it's like to go back with nothing gained, a supplicant rather than an achiever. At least I was an absolute stranger here, incomer, outsider, and I was only reclaiming the money I'd poured into some robot machine's pockets for so many bloody years. I haven't ever been back since things went wrong. Somewhere, within me, the sleeping poetry said no, no, no.

And the Third World coterie for which I'd read my poetry had gone, too, in search of higher ground. Now I did classrooms, community centres, backwood bookshops and questions I couldn't answer. My poetic urge had been flagging for aeons, it was arthritic now. I didn't have much of a sense of community here, and you need to write from a sense of something. I couldn't keep on singing about kite festivals, first love, my daughter, Aung San Suu Kyi or South Africa. A culture had grown up among the second generation of subcontinental immigrants that I hadn't really had the time or the inclination to understand: bhangra discos and Joy Bangla and boots under shalwars and Hindi movie stars. Aneela'd said it was all a distorted copy of the real thing; I'd say now there's more to it than that. But at the time, I'd just been too busy and preoccupied with the journal, the organisation of functions and readings and Third World conferences, fatherhood, Aneela's complaint that motherhood and a busy, busy husband were cannibalising her youth . . . You could have called me self-centred, if I'd ever had enough of a self to consider. I'd just spent my life at the office and used to come home to fall into bed six days a week, and on Sundays I'd take Suhayla out and watch videos and read the papers.

When I thought the Job Centre people would shoot me if I stood in their queues for another handout, when the Third World editor-friends and favour-owers of another time had run out of all the book reviews, dance reviews, film reviews, theatre reviews and ultimately even race and public march and issue reviews, all the commissions they could give me at diminishing fees (from £70 down to £20), when even a can of beans cost too much and I'd gone down two stones in weight and owed £340 I didn't have, I found myself at Brickenshore College, Brickenshore, London, a teacher of ESL to refugees from Ethiopia, China, Iran and Vietnam. Not exactly what I'd envisaged. Three years on I'm still there, but don't feel for a moment that it's taught me a thing. I don't feel close to them, I don't feel they allay my sense of having lost my place; all I feel is heavy, a heavy trunk with withered bark and hanging branches and leaves that fall in thick, yellow piles before they ever grow. When I first joined and planned my lessons according to my ESL teacher's careful briefing, two of the students – a Laotian and Chinese – began to shout at me, told me they didn't want to learn silly, pretty things, only useful English to help them with a trade. I wanted to leave. But the Eritreans and the Poles – one of them was much older than me – wanted me to stay. And I did. For the money, for a place in life, to make sense of the heaviness of me. Work that was ugly but useful. Unlike this story of my life: that's ugly and of no use at all.

But that's not what Tahira would say. Tahira, who suddenly reappeared after years during my Easter holidays. I'd arranged a poetry reading here for her once, in my editorial days. She'd filled the hall with her poems. She was radical and lyrical and illuminating. And intimidating. You felt she was meeting us expatriates on sufferance. Later, though, when we'd met again, she was under some sort of political cloud, had published things she shouldn't, and had come here to see if she could reroute, or reroot herself, find something in this otherwhere. But her roots weren't portable. We needed each other: she a rudder in a strange land, me someone that reminded me of my dreaming days. Sometimes I think it wasn't my age or her pain or her need for friendship over intensity and passion that stopped her listening to my starving eyes. It was the call of a sky far way, it was her revolt against this alien sky. She told me I should start writing in Urdu again, writing for Pakistan, as a way, perhaps, of coming back for a while. I even think of it now: returning in anonymity, going to rest for a while with my parents, and then taking a backpack and going far, far up into the hills, starting off with Margalla. Then I'll go to Karachi to see Tahira. Because she went back. To the pain of her new wings growing, to the heaviness of her tree. Asking me to write, as soon as I could, about my life here, in English if I couldn't find the Urdu words and she'd translate it. So I began, hacking away at my bark and carving into it the initials of someone who's desired more than he's done and known longing more than love and never loved enough, someone who's tried to write without living and turned his face away from everyone for fear of being hurt, someone who's spent his days with his face pressed to glass and never learned to move or break the glass walls of his cage, like a bird that lost its tree and ended up in an aviary, or a tree that never grew branches to make a home for birds.

Mixed metaphors. Windows and walls. When I first started teaching I used to walk past a blind wall. It served no purpose, led nowhere, concealed nothing. Over the months, the graffiti on it kept changing: first it was WHOSA COMIN? SOCHY LIZM I'S A COMIN in huge letters and I used to wonder who Sochy was. Then it was KILROY WAS 'ERE. I hated the wall, because sometimes it reminded me of my attempts at poetry, writing loud protest at first and later merely trying to remind people I existed and myself that I had a name. Then one day the authorities decided to do something about it and instead of breaking it down they got a team of painters to make a mural, a gaudy scene of fake optimism with smiling children and giant daisies and daffodil sunshine. It used to make me feel like banging my head in misery because those colours were so false and heavy, purples and dingy oranges and peacock blues, and it made me want to turn away and say to hell with the job which as I write I'm probably about to lose anyway. Without redundancy money because I've only been employed on annual contracts for the three years I've been there.

Last night – this morning, really, because I'd been working on the fragment about my life well after midnight – I fell asleep and dreamed that the wall with its ghastly mural was blocking the view from my window and I had to get up to wipe off the bright paint and break it down. I took a bucket full of water and some washcloths downstairs to do the job but when I got there I found that I'd taken a bucket of paint instead and what I had to do was cover the tawdry hope on the wall with new pictures. I was about to begin when I woke up, sweating. I went to the window and of course there was no wall but the sky was heavy and grey again. The computer clock said 7:45. A June Sunday. For some reason it occurred to me that if the weather had been like that when I was in Pakistan I'd have rung up some friends and we'd have gone on a picnic, to the hills from Lahore or Islamabad, far, far out to the clean sea from Karachi. The wall was still with me and I knew what I had to do. I looked at the bald words I'd written and I sat down to write again, something for Tahira's magazine but even more for myself, from my own pleasure and pain, a dream story like those pieces Pakistani writers used to write during Zia's regime, couched in disturbing similes, in the colours of unease. My window had been, after all, my cage and my wall, keeping me from breathing, and I should write about that. In Urdu. As I wrote, rapidly, from right to left, the syllables of my lost tongue licked my skin like fires.

In my story, a young painter meets an alluring pair, a wise old man and his beautiful daughter, from a land across the sea. He falls in love with the daughter and apprentices himself to the old man who is one of his time's greatest painters. He follows them abroad. But when he reaches the strange city of his destination they take him to the top of a tower to a great room made of glass, overlooking the steeples and the spires and the rivers of the alien city. He is left with one brush and pots of paints and locked into the room. The old man tells him he must paint a living masterpiece on the glass walls within eleven days, when they will come back to redeem him: only then will he be worthy of their esteem, the old man's tutelage, the young woman's love. He begins on the third day, after three days of desolation. He begins from the right corner, painting a street of the city of his exile, a street he can only see from the distance of his fourteenth-floor room over rooftops and chimneys. A river runs around the room. Down a tree-lined avenue, a loving couple walk: he small and slender, she tall and very, very fat. On the platform of a little station stands a young man from the Far East, with a finger in his ear. On another street corner there's a pub, with a bench outside and a young ginger-headed man sitting on it with a giant mug of beer in his left hand. He looks at a girl who throws in the air a red scarf, dancing, dancing. Two children, a boy and a girl, point an airgun at a pigeon in a tree.

When the painter stops painting, the glass walls are nearly covered: the setting sun's rays bring everything to life, colours dance around him, their tones rebelling against the shades he's chosen. But there's still a lack. Who, he asks himself, is looking at all this: where is the centre of my scene? His paints are finished: he will have to use the yields of his body, blood and sweat and other, darker fluids. His fine brush is broken. He paints with his fingers. At the top right-hand corner of the room he paints a giant tree, gnarled, rich with green leaves: the home of birds, sparrows and humble flying things, even butterflies, though he wonders if butterflies can actually reach its branches. He stops, and looks at his work. Perhaps he sleeps for a while, for when he comes back to himself he's on the street, seated beneath his tree. He begins to walk. As he passes the pub, the ginger-haired man, now flushed with beer, spits twice, once to the right of the painter's right shoe, once to the left of his left shoe. The painter walks on. The pigeon has fallen from its tree, shot by the playful children; it lies in a knot of blood and sinew and feather and bone. He walks on. The red dancer has gone. A saxophonist stands in her place, playing music that reminds him of fire in an autumn garden. Faces he hasn't painted assail him. A young man accosts him and asks: Do you want to do business? Business? he says, and he wonders whether the young man will set him up as a pavement artist, for he knows he is dreaming, and in dreams people read your mind. But I want to sell you my corpse, says the young man, because I got off a ship from Romania ten days ago and I need money for cigarettes and new shoes. But I don't want your body, the painter says, and I have nothing to give you, my table is bare, my pockets are empty. He walks on, but his footsteps are faster. At the next corner he sees the fat woman. Her thin lover lies on the stones with blood on his forehead. Seated on his chest, the woman batters with her fists her lover's shoulders, chanting all the while: But I love you, you swine, you bastard. I do, I love you. The painter walks on. The man from the East who stood smiling on the platform stands outside the station now. He looks at what he finds in his ears, blows gently, and repeats the gesture: now he explores his nose, now he picks at his scalp, always blowing, blowing at his fingers. He asks the painter for a cigarette. I have nothing, says the painter, I am a stranger here. Then you can have one of my films, says the man from the East handing him a parcel, because I like you am a stranger, and since we can't pay for women to love, my two friends and I watch images of other people making love every night when we go home from work in the restaurant kitchen, to the attic room we share. I don't want your film, the painter says. He walks on. He's back at the tree where he started, but his shoes are heavy with mulch, and the season must have changed, for piles of leaves lie beneath the tree, nesting small dead things. He stops. The shadows of the city fall on him through the glass. His painting sleeps again. He is breathless, exhausted. He knows his eleven days are over now. No one has come to redeem him. He knows now that the woman who had enchanted him was the old man's lover, not his daughter. The old man will teach him nothing. He's a captive in this glass tower. The colours of the street he has painted, painted on glass, are fading. Forms merge with the deepening night. He clings to the tree, drawing on its heaviness for succour, but it's only a tracery of painted lines on glass. Then he hears thunder, and a crack of blue lightning hits the window. Branches push against the glass, looking for rain and light. He hears the glass smash about him. The tower falls but that doesn't matter. Warm drops of light shower my bark, the rain pours its blue sap on me. My tree still stands. Green leaves burst from my skin, green shoots explode from me. Rivulets of light run through my fingers. I hear the sound of wings in my ears as migrant birds on their way to the south make their nests in my green head. In anticipation of the deluge, I raise my hands. My fresh raw limbs reach outwards, to talk to the punishing and the pardoning sky.

The River of Return

Joan Riley

When she was a young girl just turned fourteen her grandfather told her about the secret magic of river water. Sitting on the grassy bank of the mighty Galina on the eve of his death he held Juno's hands in his withered ones and told her why he came home after thirty-eight years abroad. He had let his shadow fall across the fringes of the water at that very spot just before the sun slipped over the horizon thirty-nine years before. It took a lifetime but because he wanted it hard enough he came back home to where his shadow lay.

She chose the Harlem river, because Harlem was the place in America she most wanted to call her own. Moving furtively among the rocks, avoiding the fringe religious groups at pray and the children at play, she let her shadow creep stealthily across the riverbank until it slipped silently into the murky shallows.

Juno wanted the States too hard to wait a lifetime like her grandfather. Wanted to become an American citizen while she was young enough to enjoy the pace and reap the fruits of the American Dream. For three years she hungered for New York, but she waited, ignoring offers of illegal entry, biding her time. She wanted to do it properly. *Start as you mean to go on*, she kept telling herself, as she bombarded family and friends with begging letters and scored the job pages for that legal opportunity. She had cast her shadow on the waters and she was unshakeable in the belief that *her* time would come.

Her first trip had been a holiday. A dream she saved for four years from her meager wage as grade school teacher to realise. Her uncle had been living in New York, happy to put her up on the sofabed in his small one-bedroom apartment. He was caretaker to three buildings near 131st and Lennox and the apartment came with the job.

Uncle Sam was a strange man. He had married a woman ten years older than himself causing a scandal people still talked about, even though it was forty years in the past. They emigrated to England three years after the marriage, taking their two young children with them. He worked as a bus driver for London Transport until he could set up in business on his own. They had six more children as he prospered. Then, aged thirty-nine, he ran out on his wife to live with her nineteen-year-old cousin in the States. He had been a skilled man, a carpenter, but could not find that work in the high-rise concrete warren of New York.

The young cousin left him after eighteen months, pregnant with another man's child and making plans to marry. By then he liked New York and freedom from responsibility too much to go back to England or the Islands. He had dreams that only America could encompass and he was convinced he could make it big.

Uncle Sam's ambitions had modified as he aged. At sixty-two he gloried in the knowledge that he lived and worked in what he insisted was mid-town Manhattan. His grand boast was that he did not live in Harlem, eyes closed to the fact that the map located him squarely in that part of the city.

It was a black neighborhood on its way down, showing the scars and resentments of in-flow immigration, while hanging on grimly to its working tenants with their upwardly mobile ambitions and semi-skilled jobs. It was a little more mixed than the regimented separation she was later to find in Brooklyn, where even the different islands of the Caribbean had their own little slice of territory and accents were as much a part of the patchwork as the patriotic bunting left festooning the buildings since the last 4th of July celebrations.

She had fallen in love with the city even before she arrived, fed on a diet of boastful letters from family and friends and the fast-moving action of American television shows. Kojak with his lollipop was her particular favorite, closely followed by *Hill Street Blues*. It seemed so glamorous, so different from the prosaic everydayness of the farming community she worked and lived in.

When she arrived it was like being on a giant film set. Larger than life, and already familiar. She found herself looking out for landmarks, trying to find the places she had viewed on the small screen. It was the height of summer and the city baked without the breeze of her island to cool the grey sidewalks. The streets were loud and brash. Buzzing. Overflowing with converging streams of people rushing headlong through life. Everyone seemed richer than she'd ever dreamed was possible, eating out in McDonald's or getting pre-packed dinners only the well-off could afford back in Galina.

She didn't notice how drab and seedy Manhattan was when the neon signs gave way to daylight. She rode the buses downtown, then up towards the Bronx. Visited the World Trade Centre and Riverside Park. Walked along the fringes of Central Park afraid to enter in case she was accosted. Her uncle came with her to the UN building and the Statue of Liberty, because he had never visited them in the twenty-two years he had lived in New York.

On her own, Juno walked around Columbus Square pretending she had just been disgorged from one of the many subway exits. Snapped pictures with her Instamatic camera in Times Square, looked at the lights of Broadway, the theme tune of her favorite musical playing inside her head. She especially liked to merge with the crowds on 42nd Street and bustle into Grand Central like she too had a purpose in the city. Sometimes she would take a train to an upstate destination picked at random, marveling at the power of the river, the lush green country so close to the city. She drank thirstily of each new experience, but Harlem was *her* place. Multi-layered and dangerous as Galina could never be. It was a brooding, multilingual sprawl. Smoldering with angry passion, waiting to flare to the bleeding remains of another drug or turf incident. The broken sidewalks, and worn tarmac with its rubbish-choked holes reminded her of Majestic, the capital of her native region. Yet this was New York, with its twenty-four-hour high speed life.

Her uncle tried to show her a good time, taking her to watch a wrestling match at Madison Square Gardens and shouting himself hoarse with the excitement. He also took her to discos he was far too old to enjoy, looking uncomfortable and out of place among brash young men and skimpily dressed women. Juno watched the sleek women with envy. Her calf-length high-collar dress and short unrelaxed hair would have been more at home in church than in the night life of the city. She wanted to dress in short body-hugging clothes, several earrings in each ear, arms heavy with gold and silver bangles that jangled as she moved. She hungered for the sharp-suited equally decorated men with their gold chains, diamond-studded gold teeth and rings on every finger. It fed her determination to return, to live and work, get her Green Card so she would have a right to all of it. Juno found herself remembering her grandfather's words about the secret magic of river water. New York was a city built on many rivers and all she had to do was let her shadow fall on one.

She came back with Tim, her lover of eighteen months. He had to leave the island after some city business his brother was involved in got out of hand. For Juno, Tim was danger, excitement and a passport back to New York. He was a survivor. A thin, wiry man with a burning ambition to hit the big time in the States. He had spent five years as a mule, carrying discreet packages, double-wrapped in condoms, swallowed half a dozen at a time, to be expelled at the other end, for a thousand US dollars.

He used those years to make connections in the city. Patiently building a reputation for reliability and loyalty because he carried drugs but didn't use them.

They traveled to New York on visitors' visas. Juno was high on fear and excitement, especially when she found out Tim was carrying one last shipment. Love for him and lust for that city blinded her to the moral objections she used to have against those who trafficked drugs or became illegal in another country. They got through immigration without a hitch, though Juno was drenched with sweat by the time the official finally brought the stamp down on the stiff, rectangular card clearing her for entry.

Queens was drizzly and overcast when they finally arrived there in the late afternoon. Dank and dismal, it was different from her memories of Manhattan. They stayed two weeks with a friend of her uncle's, before moving to the apartment in a decaying tenement building Tim's sisters shared in Brooklyn. The women had a one-roomed apartment directly opposite a massive neon sign advertising everything from Moviedrome to Craven 'A'. It smelt permanently of rotting cabbage and stale vomit, despite the disinfectant they constantly sprinkled on the threadbare carpet.

New York was a hard city, especially for Tim. He had no status away from Galina and the promises of work evaporated once he lost his value as an active courier. He squandered the money he did have, on presents for his sisters, new clothes for Juno and himself and the gambling and drinking she hadn't known he was into. When the money ran out, he sat slumped on the sofabed that dominated their side of the crowded room, complaining bitterly about how much he had sacrificed for love of her.

Tasha, Tim's younger sister, found Juno a job in the small factory where she worked making functional clothes for local cheap outlets. Juno was given the task of sewing cuffs onto men's shirts, alongside two Mexican women who spoke no English. She was nearly deafened by the noise of the big industrial machines and the shouted conversations of the women crowded in the long, low-ceilinged room. By the end of the first week her throat was sore, nose constantly running, irritated by cigarette smoke and the cotton fluff that swirled around in the draft from the window vents.

The work was hard, the hours long, the pay poor even by the standard of the unqualified teacher's wages Juno used to earn in Galina. She worked twelve hours, six days a week, yet had little to show for it. She had to pay the sisters $25 for sharing the room, and Tim was forever borrowing money; always involved with one get-rich-quick scheme after another, once the initial shock of rejection had worn off.

After she paid her living expenses, she had $10 to herself. This she put in a plain brown envelope, hiding it carefully inside the sofabed. Despite the hardship, Juno was grateful for the work. She saw it as a stepping stone and no one questioned whether she had a work permit.

Four months after she started work the factory was raided and closed down. Tasha got caught and deported as an overstayer. Juno was lucky. She and the two Mexican women got out through a broken pane in the small toilet window. They managed to climb over to the fire escape of the adjoining tenement building and slip into the afternoon crowd. She was too scared to look for work for weeks after her narrow escape and then she never stayed too long in one place. Always looking over her shoulder, afraid the immigration people would raid again and she would not be so fortunate next time.

Juno survived for two and a half years moving from one casual occupation to another. She found work wherever she could. Marginal, twilight jobs where no one asked questions of origin and you could be laid off without warning if cheaper labour came along to undercut your going rate. She went from factory work to early morning and late evening cleaner, a chambermaid shuffling along the corridors of second-rate downtown hotels, working in some of the kitchens of wealthy upstate whites. The plum job had been the one in the sandwich bar: washing piles of dishes that never seemed to shrink however diligently she applied herself – but making a whole dollar fifty an hour.

She had more than thirty jobs in those two years, often two and three at a time. Some lasted no more than a week; others kept her for months. She was tired all the time, face beginning to show the strain, but no nearer to the coveted Green Card than she had been on the day she arrived.

Maybe she could have survived a little longer if the drudgery was all she had to contend with. On its own the mean existence was bearable. Things had even started to look up once she had the relative security of the sandwich bar. She was still doing late shift cleaning, and for the first time could dream of moving to her own apartment.

The other thing was different. What she mentally labeled *Tim's sideline*. It leached her self-respect a little at a time, until she was afraid she would tumble into the hopeless world of the sad-looking women that haunted the mean streets outside their building.

It started in a small way, a one-off thing to get some cash and help Tim out of a jam. He had borrowed money for another get-rich-quick scheme, then lost it in a card game. The way Tim put it was reasonable. Just a couple of guys he had hooked up with – no street corner stuff. One of them had a nice apartment and he bought her a party dress to travel in.

She felt sick afterwards. Soiled. But Tim had been grateful, penitent. He even got a *legal* job for a while, though he soon drifted back to his old ways. The second time it was money he owed a drug dealer. He used the argument that she had already done it with two of the men he was proposing.

They never talked about those nights. Tim was always extra loving afterwards, buying her little trinkets and a bottle of her favorite Mount Gay rum. Pretty soon Juno needed the rum to see her through the sessions. She got into the habit of sipping tall glasses of the amber spirit and smoking cannabis to dull the sick feeling it left her with. It oiled the wheels of her imagination, weaving fantasies around the two magic weeks she had spent with her uncle in Manhattan. She would pretend she was one of the sleek women from the disco. That one of the sharp-suited men had wined and dined her late into the night and they had finally ended in his luxury apartment. The more she drank, the more she could filter out the panting, sweaty body on top of her and lose herself in the New York of her imagination for a time.

Juno had no head for alcohol. The queasiness stayed with her most of the day following each drinking bout. Each time she let him sell her body, she lost a little more respect for both herself and Tim. Each time she made a vow there would be no next time.

One day in the height of her third summer in New York, Juno woke, in the sweltering coffin-like space she shared with Tim and his older sister Rina, and knew she had had enough. She was sick and aching, smelling of stale sex and souring alcohol and feeling lower than she could ever remember feeling.

Juno had spent most of the previous night on her back in that other flat to pay yet another gambling debt. It was the third time that week. Tim no longer even bothered with the pretense that he had any qualms about using her body as a major source of income. She knew the routine well. Today he would bring some small trinket, probably a box of chocolates, along with something nice to keep Rina sweet.

She slid off the lumpy mattress and went to peer at her face in the chipped mirror over the dressing table. She took a hard look at the new lines scouring her forehead and pinching age at the corners of her mouth and knew she was slipping fast.

Last night one of the faceless men offered her some little white crystals to liven her up. The high had been a revelation, a kaleidoscope, a sunburst inside her head. Afterwards, too short a time later, she had wanted another, then another – hardly caring about the use the man had made of her. By the end of the night, she knew she could develop a taste for the little white rocks. The concentrated intensity of those sharp fifteen minutes' high was worth any indignity – or so it seemed at the time.

Morning brought back sanity, a brief clarity about the situation she found herself in. Juno knew she would always be illegal in America. Worse off than Rina – hanging onto her dignity and working herself into the ground as she waited for that legal opportunity. Tim was pulling her down with him, preying on her with a ruthlessness she found hard to even acknowledge. Her accent, her attitude, her language betrayed her in his new world, too lacking in American street to give her credibility. To Tim's new friends, she was nothing more than another piece of meat rapidly approaching its sell-by date.

She envied the people who belonged. The black Americans with their ease of passage. Other islanders, once immigrant now turned American citizens with scarcely a vowel out of place as they policed every nuance of speech. Some offered help – with speech, with walk, with clothes, remembering their own gauche naivety when they first stepped on American soil.

Tim's walk and accent betrayed him too, but he was eager to merge into the life that had always held so much excitement for him. He spent most of his time hanging around the pimps and numbers runners, or doing odd jobs for the loan sharks that operated out of Queens. He did the numbers diligently, using every little win to buy small quantities of coke and heroin to recut and sell. He cultivated an American twang as hard as she held onto the musical softness of her island homeland once disillusionment set in.

Tim had a driving ambition to taste the American Dream, but Juno hated living in a confined space. The invisible demarcation of their part of Brooklyn surrounded by a patchwork of other nationalities and cultures was suffocating. She had come to America to seek wide horizons, get some education, buy a house and own a piece of Moviedrome. She was no nearer to any of it, no nearer to the coveted Green Card that would be a passport to a regular job with time for self-improvement.

Juno packed her bag, withdrawing the folded envelope with her meager savings from inside the sofabed. There was enough to get her a ticket back to Galina and a few presents for her mother and her auntie. She took a bus into Manhattan – the first time she had been there since moving back to New York. It didn't seem so glamorous any more. The smell of Wieners and frying onions made Juno feel queasy after her drinking bout the night before. Her jaded eyes noticed the cracked and broken sidewalks and shabby, unkempt buildings. Whole families of beggars, soiled and ragged, moved hopelessly through the crowd. She felt jostled by the rushing people on the streets as if in some way her spirit had already left for home.

Tim was stunned when he came in to find her packed and waiting for her taxi to the airport. He begged and pleaded, telling her how much he loved her, how he had not been unfaithful even once in the four years they had been together. The tears brimming in his eyes made her waver until she remembered the greed on his face as he counted the takings from the night before. She thought of the faceless men pushing into her on the oversoft mattress, fancied she could still smell them on her skin, and turned her back on him.

Her love had tarnished. Corroded. Been traded too many times to get him quick money. She closed her ears to his pleading. Hardened her heart to the tears he always saw as weakness in the past. Tim would never change. Whether he loved her or not, he had grown used to the easy money her body yielded. She still ached from the memory of the small white rocks. The intensity of the pleasure called to her, frightened her and she knew she had to leave to save her life and sanity.

Her taxi bumped along the concrete funnel, dwarfed by the massive structures of the projects, snarled up in the traffic feeding into the toll gates on the way to La Guardia airport. Juno focused on all the New York rivers she had crossed. In her mind she saw again the wide waters of the Narrows, the Hudson, the East River and the Harlem. She thought about the clear cool waters of her home rivers. The hours she spent with her grandfather on the lush banks of the Galina or stood fishing in its shallows, her shadow merging with the old man's across the river of return . . .

Circles

Pierre Tran

We took the number 84 double-decker bus, wound our way through the suburbs of north London and crossed a green and pleasant land to arrive at St Albans, Hertfordshire. That was to be our family home for the next twenty years.

It seems to me that that bus trip was the beginning of a second life and that I left behind a life – and a language – in Vietnam.

What does Vietnam conjure up for you?

Napalm, gunships, burning villages and bodies of dead Vietcong?

For me, in the early sixties, there was no 'Vietnam war' to burst into a carefree childhood in what was then Saigon. True, there was an uncle, an army officer who fondly placed on my head his peaked cap heavy with braid when he visited.

One day, in the heat of the Saigon afternoon, there was word of paratroopers landing in the city. I strained my eyes to see their white canopies but only saw a clear blue sky.

Outside our cool spacious house, there was a policeman who wore a pistol and I carefully hovered nearby, eyes on stalks, trying to glimpse the butt under the holster.

There were summer holidays in the cool of the mountain resort, Dalat, or in the house rented by the beach. We hunted for crab in the night, by torchlight – electric torch – and with nets. We rode the wild white surf on huge rubber inner tubes, safe on the gently shelving yellow sand. There was a war, but it was in the countryside and we lived charmed lives, punctuated by late-night barbecues when my older brother and I would stay up and share peanuts meagrely, to make them last.

There was a barber who cut our hair outdoors. I endured the *snip snip* of his scissors, helped by watching the chicks and goslings which ran freely around our feet on the flagged path in front of his house.

We slept under mosquito nets, with bolsters, and were tended by a nanny who unselfishly lavished attention on me, who was then the youngest of three. I am told I returned her unstinting affection by giving her major mischief. One hot night, unable to sleep, I woke up and wandered round the silent house and found her, outside, washing herself by the water tub. What long hours she must have worked, to be cleaning herself when the household had retired.

Although I don't remember it, I spent a lot of time seriously ill. That was the life we left, when my parents brought us to the England of the sixties.

The winter of 1963. What a delight for a small boy newly arrived from a tropical country. We donned balaclavas, turned up anorak hoods and discovered snow – and in what quantities undreamt of. Banks of snow, roads piled high with snow, a pure whiteness of snow – and of course, the art of the snowball. This was going to be a great country to live in.

St Albans before the 1980s property boom was a quiet, prosperous city which wore its history proudly. It is not the county seat – that honour belongs to Hertford – but as Verulamium, it was the capital of Roman Britain. It has an ancient abbey Cathedral, a minor public school, a street market and feeds London's appetite for office workers who each morning commuted into St Pancras station.

It was a safe place to grow up, with a mixture of middle-class neighbourhoods and council estates whose occupants largely stuck to their apportioned grammar schools or secondary moderns. And all around stretched the rich farmlands and Georgian country houses, protected by the post-war planning restrictions of the Green Belt.

St Alban's & St Stephen's: a strict but caring Catholic primary school whose nuns and lay teachers poured their energies into getting their charges to the best schools possible.

Imperceptibly I learned English and gradually withdrew from my native Vietnamese tongue.

There was a library in the town centre, one of hundreds endowed by the Scottish-American millionaire robber baron, Andrew Carnegie, where I drew my quota of two books religiously every Saturday. My compositions gained notice and got my place at a grammar school.

Like every English boy I played football, running in the summer heat, breathing in the grass-scented air, my white school uniform shirt sticking to my back.

There were rebellions against school rules and a constant questioning of authority.

And on the television, as we grew up, there was Vietnam – not the one I left behind but a place of atrocities, the Tet Offensive, the visitations of war and slaughter. It was like living a shadow life: instead of living the one I was meant to live by reason of birth and nationality, by race and origin, here I was, studying Scott of the Antarctic and the Poor Law reforms and listening to 'Bridge over Troubled Waters'.

Time, *Newsweek*, the *Sunday Times* carried articles reporting the war which were consumed with a teenage superficial understanding. Although we had come from Saigon, South Vietnam, we sided with the North and believed the Americans were the interlopers. I still do believe that.

I became almost-English, without being English, by making English language and literature my own. I was Vietnamese but no-longer-Vietnamese because I had lost my own tongue.

George Bernard Shaw's *Pygmalion*, seized on as an early

favourite, describes what it might be like to be lost in your own country, cast adrift by an accent. Eliza gains an accent but loses her soul – 'What's to become of me?' she asks despairingly. To which Higgins has no fit reply. She must make, or re-make, her own life.

My brothers and sisters and I grew up among the English but we never lost our sense of being Vietnamese, if only because there were the constant reminders that we were different. That's to say, even as we were losing the positive identifier of nationality – our language – we still had the negative truth of looking foreign, heaven help us! We were identifiably not-English.

So growing up was a precarious existence among the casual cruelty of children taunting 'Chinese, Japanese, dirty knees.' Other gems were 'We are Siamese if you please,' with the inevitable pulling of the chanter's eyelids, or the unimaginative but brutally effective 'Chinky'. And yet, there are remembered moments of pure kindness, of simple goodness – a white-haired couple, our neighbours in those early St Albans days, who cared for us as their own grandchildren, for we never knew our own grandparents.

Now, moving among the English professional classes there is nothing so indelicate as the racial insults. Instead there is that polite enquiry, 'Are you from Singapore/Hong Kong/ Malaysia?' – or any south-east Asian country which springs to the mind of the interrogator. Even recently, an apparently intelligent executive barged into a meeting, loud-mouthed, large, proudly showing his ignorance with the usual question – 'Where are you from?' and proceeded to reel off countries where the overseas Chinese have made their home for centuries – he listed a handful, except, of course, China and Vietnam.

He naturally thinks I am Chinese – well I must be, must I not? As I look oriental, so I am Chinese; but he cannot come out and ask me the question direct. Heaven forfend! that would be too direct for an English gentleman so we must go through the dance of guess-the-country-of-origin. And then to my answer of Vietnam, he brightly volunteers he has been there.

Yes, my good man, you were certainly there but you learned no great deal, not even to think before you speak.

Identity is what the migrant leaves behind. The identity that is endowed by shared colour and culture, neighbourhood, a community, a religion, a dialect. In the new world, a new identity. And misunderstanding, incomprehension and intolerance.

Why should it matter that people mistake me for Chinese? Are we not of the same racial stock, sharing physical characteristics, an alphabet and a philosophical system?

It matters.

The original peoples of what is now called Vietnam were conquered, hunted and pushed into the forests and highlands by the invading settlers from the north, China.

But over hundreds of years those settlers in the south formed kingdoms of their own and fought the rule of the Middle Kingdom of China. They formed a distinct culture and language and became a separate people.

They fought for their own identity.

For the best part of a millennium, the people of the south, the Smaller Dragon, Vietnam, defied the greater Dragon of China.

Later they fought the French, the Japanese and latterly the Americans. Who can be whole when someone denies you a sense of who you are and what you are? Are you free to let others define you? Strip away all material things and identity is all that is left.

And what of the life we left behind?

My paternal grandfather was a mandarin, a chief of Ben Tre province in the centre of Vietnam, at a time when it was a protectorate of France and the French relied on Vietnamese administrators to interpret and implement their rule. His word was law.

Doubtless the French could have imposed their system without the aid of such as my grandfather but I like to think it would have been a harsher form of colonialism without the mediation of those who knew infinitely more about the people and the land than their rulers from the metropolitan centre.

From my father's family came a foreign minister, an

ambassador – and a niece who became the sister-in-law of the late President Diem: Madame Nhu, the 'Dragon Lady'.

My maternal grandfather served in the French army and rose to officer rank. A grateful Republic rewarded him with French citizenship, which he passed on to his children. Her father, in turn, went to France for his education and became a surveyor, a member of the technical elite, part of the privileged, educated urban Vietnamese who benefited from the French imperium and went to form the backbone of the nationalist revolution. My mother became the third generation to drink from the fountain of French culture, also going to Paris for her education, helped by her brothers – for by now the Second World War had disrupted the family finances. In a French *lycée* in the tropics, she learned about 'Nos ancêtres, les Gaulois' – our ancestors the Gauls; she spoke and wrote the language of Descartes and Rousseau perfectly, while at home she learned her native Vietnamese.

From her brothers came, variously, an ambassador for the North, an architect, a leader of the Vietcong – the political arm of the South Vietnamese resistance, a judge and the army officer who put his cap on my head when he visited. He became a national hero, a colonel coup-maker, a plotter and conspirator who impressed all who met him with his quickness and intelligence and who died in a torturer's cell, after a coup too many. So from this, the war was a constant companion to our childhood even in the darkest heart of the English Home Counties.

The war was not a lived but a learned experience. There was a copy of Felix Greene's book of the war. It had stark black and white photography of tortures inflicted by South Vietnamese and American troops on Vietcong suspects or sympathisers. Here is a man, bound and slowly disembowelled with a knife. Here is a man being drowned. Another is being crushed by an armoured personnel carrier.

They are acts of dehumanising atrocity done by anonymous men, yet who have a name and habitation, who perhaps went home to families but left their victims in unmarked graves.

Who knows what acts were committed in the North in

the name of national unification? No camera or campaigning journalist recorded the suffering of those unfortunates.

The reporting of that war impressed on me the infinite cruelty of mankind. Twenty years later I can still remember the article which described so-called anti-personnel devices – not bombs, mark you – which contained razor-sharp plastic fragments designed to penetrate the body and wound without killing. They were made of plastic so they could not be found by X-rays. What brilliant researcher conceived of that tiny refinement to human endeavour? Did he patent it before selling it to a grateful company? Or was he a staff employee on a fixed salary? Perhaps there was a performance bonus for recognition of a job well done. Or was there merely professional pride in solving a tricky problem of how to lower troop morale and burden soldiers with a hideously maimed colleague?

And which genius thought of calling those fragments 'flechettes' – cute-sounding, harmless little arrows, not even fully fledged big weapons, yet resonant of the human flesh they were designed to tear apart? Reflect that no evil spirit but a human brain and hand conjured up the means of that unplumbable pain. 'O brave new world that has such scientists in it!'

Against the Western industrial capacity for manufacturing carnage, the oriental flair for innovation cries out for recognition. The homely cottage industry of the jungle fighter made the punji stick, a sharpened bamboo spiked with excrement which sliced through an army boot and poisoned the body with corrupt matter.

All wars are dirty wars, but I grew up with the Vietnam war. My alternative education was an awful taxonomy of weaponry and the now familiar litany of towns which were sites of terrible battles.

And yet, after all that destructive energy released on a mainly civilian population, there was no peace with honour – only an American ambassador with a furled flag hastily boarding a helicopter and a legacy of millions of individual stories of human loss and suffering.

In the house that Jack built, there are torture chambers and charnel houses and the garden is a graveyard of the unknown victim. Jack is handy with his cunning inhumanity, always devising new and terrifying means of imposing darkness, but the story is always the same in whatever country or community – the powerful consume the weak.

The war in Vietnam was a long time ago and a new generation has grown up without experience of the war. Some 40 per cent of the 67-million-strong population are under fifteen years of age and the most urgent issue for today's leaders is to improve living standards for some of the poorest people in the world. The economy is now what matters.

All those terrible things happened a long time ago and people need to move on in their lives – or else how could they function? But nothing ever really goes away, the trauma simply sinks below the conscious. A nation has no right to forget the suffering of its people. But if it does not move forward and prefers to live in the past, it has written off its future.

Human sacrifice is the oldest appeasement to the gods. The victims are the innocent. Where are the barber and the nanny of my childhood? What became of them and their families? I am a survivor and they say it is the survivor who is condemned to feel guilt for escaping the fate of his fellow. But don't forget there is anger, too. The survivor is also an angry person, raging inside against the loss through theft and violence.

Now, with young children of my own, half-French and half-Vietnamese but born in this country, I go with them on Saturdays to re-learn my own language. I sit with my beautiful Claire and Celine, alongside Linda, Thao, Elizabeth and the other round-cheeked, bright-eyed, smiling faces and repeat the musical tones of our teacher, Thinh. They sing little songs to help learn the subtle inflections and cadences of each word, while at the next table, the older children learn maths and geometry – in Vietnamese, of course – from Ly. Close your eyes and cast your mind back and this could almost be a village classroom in Vietnam. This is Lewisham, south-east London, but a piece of Vietnam lives on here.

From a Diary

Adam Lively

7 June 1984, Salem, Oregon

Fishing in the foothills of the Cascades. A different relationship between man and nature. Here nature is generous (she can still afford to be) – a bridge, a highway, is an allowance made to man, handed down generously by the imperious hills. It is those hills that dominate. The rushing river by which we sat was guided by those green hulks. Tall pines cling to their steeps, and we, crouched in the rain, are enfolded in their damp greenness. A mythic grouping – the two men crouched in the rain, the rushing water, the fishing poles, the damp greenness.

America. Most of the clichés are true – it's just that there are depths to those truisms. The land of instant myths. The combination of a compulsive affirmation of what *is* with a desire that brute reality should instantaneously become a myth, a dream, an ideal, something transcendent. Easy to suggest a pathology: it reveals a profound disgust with the reality one is creating. (To make reality into a dream is to evade responsibility for it.)

11 June 1984, Salem, Oregon

Walking through the woods at Cascade Head – the dappled light flowing down Greg's back like water into still pools on the leafy ground. And then returning along the same path: a beetle crosses the path just as my huge foot falls inches from it, and the insect veers away before disappearing again on its journey. Thus contact was made at the fading edges of God knows what universe my foot entered and was met and enveloped and judged and for a moment we danced together and (who knows?) despite all they say perhaps the beetle too even now if it still lives somewhere out there carries traces as I do of that moment.

13 June 1984, Salem, Oregon

A true story I heard on the local radio station yesterday: some time earlier this century a couple of men tried to hold up a train near Salem. They botched the hold-up and killed the driver. Later they were captured and brought back here. They were sentenced to life in the town penitentiary. And for the rest of the lives, every train that passed the penitentiary, the driver would blow his whistle, to taunt the men in their cell. Thought about that story last night, the window open in the heat, listening to a train passing in the distance. Found myself thinking about the other times I've heard trains at night.

29 June 1984, Salem, Oregon

Walking down Court Street from the apartment in the rain. Filled with shame and self-hatred. And then I had to stand waiting for a freight train to pass. It took about five minutes – the longest train I've ever seen – and as it passed, and as I read off the names on the wagons (Cotton Belt, Southern Pacific, Georgia Freight) my anguish drained away. It was the thought of travel, of freedom. Also, rain can be cheering at times.

3 July 1984: eve of the nation's birthday, Salem, Oregon

Stifling heat and the sound of fireworks going off around town. Depression all day – partly a bad hangover. Ashamed of my behaviour last night – very drunk and pontificating in a silly way about politics and America. I think my anti-Americanism is picked up by and offends people more than I'm usually aware.

'America: love it or leave it' (redneck saying). Nothing is more unpleasant than to dislike oneself.

More fireworks. A celebration in which I have no part. With evening coming on, the depression melting into pleasurable melancholia.

15 August 1984, Framingham, Massachusetts

Sitting on a suburban patio, I hear a dog barking in the next door yard. And in the distance, far over a leafy hill, another dog replies from another yard. On this summer afternoon, in this American suburb, the dogs have the still air to themselves. Only occasionally the sound of a car.

A friend from England who visited me a while ago wrote to me later of a sense of eeriness he'd felt while in America. He struggled to define it but couldn't – it was a feeling of unreality, a feeling that there was something about America that could not be grasped. But I knew exactly what he meant. An example: across the road from the apartment where I stayed in Salem was a squat, ugly church. Every evening there would be a peal of bells from the church, only there was something not right about these bells. Then one evening I realised that they weren't real bells at all – it was a tape recording of bells being played through loudspeakers in the tower. I became obsessed with those bells, listening to them every evening and trying to imagine where they were, those real bells that weren't in the church across the road.

The apartment was just round the corner from the state mental hospital. An enormous, forbidding building – someone told me that Oregon has the highest rate of mental illness in the country, because so many of the people live in rural isolation. And this is where they fetch up. (Ken Kesey used it as the setting of *One Flew Over the Cuckoo's Nest.*) A few of the houses in my street were half-way hostels for people being released back into the community. All day – and all night – sad-looking, gibbering characters walked round and round the block. I used to watch them, got to recognise them. In the evening the sunset stretched out wide beyond the state capitol building. The bells.

Those people slowly passing. One night a spectacular electrical storm. No rain, just a heavy pressure in the air.

25 September 1984, New Haven, Connecticut

America is a great Cheshire cat of a nation. The more I scrutinise it, the more it seems to dissolve, leaving only a bland smile. Why – for whom – is it smiling?

10 October 1984, New Haven, Connecticut

The light playing on my wall at night. The shadows in Plato's cave. The dreams that slide over the smooth surface of America. Which is the light, which is the shadow? It can't be grasped. Always the feeling that something has not been understood. This feeling is not simply the rootlessness of the alien. There is a lack of solidity here. Everything is up in the air.

Even if we look to the future, we must look to it as to a reality. We must gather it in to ourselves, not leave it hanging, dangling, as a hope, an idea. And people themselves must never become just ideas (personhood, identity, natural rights, etc.), for all ideas come *from* them. Our task is to bring to consciousness the source of our ideas – a never-ending task.

9 December 1984, New Haven, Connecticut

Outside my window an immense stars-and-stripes unfurls in the bitter winter air. As it rolls and unfolds it seems to have a life of its own. It is set against the washed blue of a freezing winter afternoon. It dominates the indistinct New England landscape. The more I look at it, the more foreign I feel, the more it feels a part of the coldness. As I look, it has been lowered – now there is not even that to brighten the view from my window.

The coldness extends across the world. I have withdrawn into my warmth, but at the edges I still touch a cold world. I would like not to touch it at all. The clouds are pink and pulled-at by the cold air. The coldness puts a distance between things. There is here and there is there, but in between it is cold. Most of all there is a lack of movement.

11 December 1984, New Haven, Connecticut

A memory of Oregon. For hours one day I watched three ospreys hunting along a crowded beach. The bathers were oblivious to them, probably thinking they were just gulls. I stood with my feet sinking into the wet sand, tracking them with my binoculars. The ospreys soared at about a hundred feet, only now and then moving the air with their broad, crooked wings. All the time they scanned the water with heads bent, like scholars at their desks. They passed close to me – close enough to see the brown back, the pale underparts, the black markings on the shoulder of the wing, the piratical stripe through the eye. And then a shudder would run through one of the birds, a quiver of excitement, and it would deliberately stall its flight. The descent is swift but careful: the eyes fixed on the target, the wings drawn in somewhat, the osprey coming down in spiralling bursts like a man descending a cliff by rope. All the time a balance between the eyes drawing the bird on to its food and the wings playing the air to control the fall. Just before meeting the water (some three seconds after that shudder when the fish is first seen) the rear is brought forward and the massive claws lowered like the wheels of a landing jumbo jet. In the water – out of its element – the osprey is like a bird in distress, the wings flapping wildly. Beneath the surface I can imagine the claws groping (blindly now) for their prey. A second or two later the bird lifts off again with a steelhead twisting in its talons. The fish flashes in the sunlight. For a moment, as the osprey rises with wings outstretched from an aura of foam and spray, it is like a phoenix rising from its own ashes.

Skin

Fred D'Aguiar

1

I am a free man. This means nothing to anyone since there has never been a slave. Am I making sense? I say to you, I am a free man since there has never been a slave.

2

My life is like this or like that without this thing, this slavery. I meet a stranger from another sea, another climate altogether, and he sees not my skin, not me in a field he owns, but someone with whom he can trade words or deeds or secrets.

3

I am thinking too fast for myself. To assume that my skin carries no premium feels unthinkable. Yet here I am in what some call, erroneously, an extension of Europe, this America (that like a good extension has a separate entrance and exit and has little now to do with the main house) with no debt attached to my skin, no price tag on it, no investment by someone else that I must pay and repay with my labour, and at some time, my life.

4

My head spins. The premise I entertain is a carousel that turns and induces lightheadedness, giddiness. At first the revolutions are gentle. I do not need to hold onto anything to steady myself. Then I notice I am leaning and have to reach out and grip the nearest thing. My thighs tighten around the carousel which has speeded up. Instead of sticking at a breakneck pace the idea of something that has occupied the best part of 300 years suddenly begins to undo itself in earnest. Each revolution of that carousel subtracts a minute, hour and day from slavery. I hold on with all my might. (There is no way I will allow myself to be expelled from this process of reversal.) Until I get to the point in time when I was never a slave in this land and then I have to answer new questions. How else did I get here? What do I do here? Do I intend to stay?

5

This reversal in time, circumstance and fortune has made my skin weightless. I appear to float instead of walk. Gravity relinquishes its hold on me. The eye of a needle passes over me. I pour out of doors and windows and adopt the shape and colour of whatever I sit on or stand beside. How my bones feel hollow! The ground's slightest tilt or rumble makes me fly to safety with the animals and birds when not even a murmur registers on a Richter scale. I feel the varying intensities of light, from its lukewarm beginnings in the morning, to its midday boiling and afternoon malaise. Each hand held up to the light resembles a veined, translucent leaf. This skin, my skin is the adornment of all things.

6

Gravity held me captive once. No. More accurately, captured my skin, and since I am in my skin, held me. My skin was not at fault. What others said about it and then what I came to believe, based on what others had said, was to blame. My bones ached with the weight of mobility under this presumed gravity. I thought my heart would burst with the strain of pumping blood under such pressure and in such tight, heavy skin. To raise a smile I had to concentrate as if I were trying to move an object with my will alone. Now I smile as a condition of restfulness and stop or alter that expression into varieties of itself. There are as many words for smile in my vocabulary as the Eskimo has for snow, an Alaskan for light and an Amazonian for green, all combined, including the predilection of the English for discussing the weather.

7

My skin is not only porous, does not simply breathe, it has a voice; it hums, sings, intones. When a breeze brushes past it, I hear melodies. When light swims clear of cloud and washes over me, it is as if someone, tuning a Cathedral organ, has depressed several keys at once, startling the pigeons in the eaves. In the rain I am renewed.

8

I meet others like me and we marvel at our new condition and wonder what to do, besides revel in it. We wonder how the years, the generations of burdensomeness, caused by the penalty attached to the skin, how they can be repaired, revised, reversed even, so that all those lives can be lived in flotation, in glory of a heart that beats, lungs that breathe, and the brain's intricate rhythms, solutions, experiments, and none of them hampered by the skin they're in, none of them held back by attached weights, all drawing strength, sustenance, from the skin's impartial love of the atmosphere, by which I mean, all things under the sun, without exception.

9

I am not suggesting that suddenly, abracadabra, blackness is stripped of all its usual connotations, but, rather, that this new condition of weightlessness, brought about by imagining the premise that slavery never existed, has bequeathed onto blackness everything humanly possible and more besides. I am not born with hurts I spend the rest of my life failing to comprehend or combat, and for which I overcompensate.

10

As a consequence, I can barely stop myself from floating. The wonder is I do not float away entirely from this world: I am talking, not about invisibility, but visibility without a rap sheet. My life is mine to celebrate for the first time, without the tarnish of slavery as a precursor. Therefore, I go back through time and release all the souls in perpetual torment, with a kind word about the trap of skin colour. These souls rise from shallow graves, mass graves, sea burials, from being drowned, lynched, shot, flogged, burned, and other desecrations of the body; they are resurrected, and their wounds heal and they begin the life they were robbed of, without annals about their skin as a passport of penalties. They rise and float. The air makes music on their skin. Rain renews them. They pass a forest and become its pine or birch or oak or chestnut. They register one of a variety of smiles. If water comes to their eyes it is for joy or sorrow at a skin that has had its time and passes into the earth in peace. They seek a true communion with all living things.

11

I must begin (before I run too far ahead of myself) at the beginning, with the original ship that anchored off the Gold Coast, on a mission whose objective I am about to reverse. Hawking. The dead are in that name some will say. Maybe so. He has incurred enough debt to keep someone in leg irons for life. When I shake his hand, it is heavy with this debt. He is here on this coast, my coast, not for riches alone, not fame alone, but for his salvation. He was foolish enough to gamble on greed and it has brought him here, empty-handed, except for this handshake, full of the weight of debt and the dampness of a man who is poised on the brink of failure and therefore ruled by a head full of desperate impulses.

12

We hold hands for a while, this Hawking and I. I can feel him weighing up what to do next. I leap into the gap opened by his confusion. Remember I am weightless. I don't owe anyone a thing. I am not the one who has gone somewhere he knows nothing about, at great expense to himself. I was here, on this shore, when his ship was indistinguishable from cloud and then darkened and detached itself from the horizon and finally loomed up on these shores. Who would not be curious? I considered walking out to sea to greet it, but I am a man who has lived this encounter before. I know the outcome if these people are surprised or are not in control (or at least do not believe they are in control). Cannons, swords, pistols, knives, whips, irons, the auction block, bloodhounds, and all the paraphernalia of his proposed trade, all are imprinted on my skin and bone. That's why I am here again facing this man on his maiden voyage to Africa, a man who is intent on returning to his land with riches and specimens and by that inaugurate the shadow over my epoch.

13

I hold his hand and tell him there is much for him to see and little time if he is to catch the favourable winds out of here. His tongue is familiar, but I speak with my hands and diagrams in the sand and words he doesn't know, in answer to his endless questions about the locations of gold and men and women like me. He shows me what he has for this trade he intends to do with me. He wants to meet the big man (his phrase) of my people. I tell him this land is so big it takes many big people to preside over it and even then there are vast tracts of it that cannot be governed. How so? he asks. I try to describe an unending desert and a forest with many beginnings and no end and a river that can be mistaken for the sea.

14

He is intrigued. I think he likes me, or at least is fascinated with me sufficiently to dispel, for the time being, his demands to see the biggest man in the land. I do everything I can, not to float about him and his gruff crew. When I handle their weapons I use my fingertips, since my new condition of weightlessness has the added gift of abnormal powers of persuasion over inanimate objects: to tie the barrel of a gun into a knot all I need to do is press lightly on it in the right places.

15

I explain the principle of fair trade. His face falls. I make it clear to him and his men made even more indolent by the heat, that his guns cannot penetrate the swamps between these shores and the proper interior. I point to a mountain in the distance and tell him we have a weapon trained on his ship from there, one powerful enough to sink his ship and keep him here for the rest of his days. Imagine Hawking, a naturalised alien of the Gold Coast! I ask him into his incredulous face if he cares for a demonstration on one of his smaller vessels. He steps back from me and commands his men to seize me. They grab my arms, suddenly alive at the prospect of some cruel sport. He asks if I am the big man. I say there is no one by that title in this land. He handles me roughly and I let him. I repeat that he should pick a small boat before I choose one he values more highly and sink it. He points distractedly to a boat full of provisions. I tell him he should unload it first. But he insists I give him this demonstration of mine before he runs me through. I ask him to tell me how he managed to persuade his Queen to part with one of her ships. He is startled.

16

Hawking, don't be startled. I know how you got here and I know why you are here and I don't like either. I am here to save you from yourself. But I am also here to save an epoch. Now your men have released my arms through no desire of their own. Now I float above you all and most of them fall to their knees and peer up at me over a raised forearm or through their spread fingers. You order them to fire on me. Some are frozen in various aspects of shock. Others scatter into the sea or the swamps. A few open fire. I have been here before so their shots sail in and out of me without effect. Hawking, you cannot bring yourself to kneel, but your teeth chatter when you try to speak and no words issue from your mouth.

17

I lower myself to the ground. You reach out and touch my weightless skin. I ask you if you are willing to unburden yourself of the responsibility of greed, knowing full well you are not. You draw your pistol, fire at close range into my face, my smile, dash your pistol to the sand, draw your sword, thrust, and thrust again, and only desist out of breathlessness. Then you fall to your knees and sob. Poor Hawking. You thought only to serve your God and your Queen and your hungry soul. I don't want your servitude, Hawking. Listen. What you are about to embark upon cannot happen, must not happen. You, too, can be easy as air and water in your skin. But you must lose one or two things first. One is greed. The other is your quest for people of this land to serve you.

18

I ask too much? No Hawking, life is too sweet to deny it of any man, woman or child. Take my hand. Tell your men this voyage will return to England with treasure and commissioners from this land, in time. Remind them that their weapons are useless and everything here is free, so long as they take only what they need. Look, the surrounding hills are full of eyes, watching their every move. Inform them not to put anything to the test unless they do not value their lives. Where were we Hawking in our talk about fair trade?

The Tenant

Bharati Mukherjee

Maya Sanyal has been in Cedar Falls, Iowa, less than two weeks. She's come, books and clothes and one armchair rattling in the smallest truck that U-Haul would rent her, from New Jersey. Before that she was in North Carolina. Before that, Calcutta, India. Every place has something to give. She is sitting at the kitchen table with Fran drinking bourbon for the first time in her life. Fran Johnson found her the furnished apartment and helped her settle in. Now she's brought a bottle of bourbon which gives her the right to stay and talk for a bit. She's breaking up with someone named Vern, a pharmacist. Vern's father is also a pharmacist and owns a drugstore. Maya has seen Vern's father on TV twice already. The first time was on the local news when he spoke out against the selling of painkillers like Advil and Nuprin in supermarkets and gas stations. In the matter of painkillers, Maya is a universalist. The other time he was in a barbershop quartet. Vern gets along all right with his father. He likes the pharmacy business, as business goes, but he wants to go back to graduate school and learn to make films. Maya is drinking her first bourbon tonight because Vern left today for San Francisco State.

'I understand totally,' Fran says. She teaches Utopian Fiction and a course in Women's Studies and worked hard to get

Maya hired. Maya has a PhD in Comparative Literature and will introduce writers like R. K. Narayan and Chinua Achebe to three sections of sophomores at the University of Northern Iowa. 'A person has to leave home. Try out his wings.'

Fran has to use the bathroom. 'I don't feel abandoned.' She pushes her chair away from the table. 'Anyway, it was a sex thing totally. We were good together. It'd be different if I'd loved him.'

Maya tries to remember what's in the refrigerator. They need food. She hasn't been to the supermarket in over a week. She doesn't have a car yet and so she relies on a corner store – a longish walk – for milk, cereal, and frozen dinners. Someday these exigencies will show up as bad skin and collapsed muscle tone. No folly is ever lost. Maya pictures history as a net, the kind of safety net travelling trapeze artists of her childhood fell into when they were inattentive, or clumsy. Going to circuses in Calcutta with her father is what she remembers vividly. It is a banal memory, for her father, the owner of a steel company, is a complicated man.

Fran is out in the kitchen long enough for Maya to worry. They need food. Her mother believed in food. What is love, anger, inner peace, etc., her mother used to say, but the brain's biochemistry. Maya doesn't want to get into that, but she is glad she has enough stuff in the refrigerator to make an omelette. She realises Indian women are supposed to be inventive with food, whip up exotic delights to tickle an American's palate, and she knows she should be meeting Fran's generosity and candor with some sort of bizarre and effortless counter-move. If there's an exotic spice store in Cedar Falls or in neighboring Waterloo, she hasn't found it. She's looked in the phone book for common Indian names, especially Bengali, but hasn't yet struck up culinary intimacies. That will come – it always does. There's a six-pack in the fridge that her landlord, Ted Suminski, had put in because she'd be thirsty after unpacking. She was thirsty, but she doesn't drink beer. She probably should have asked him to come up and drink the beer. Except for Fran she hasn't had anyone over. Fran is more friendly and helpful than anyone

Maya has known in the States since she came to North Carolina ten years ago, at nineteen. Fran is a Swede, and she is tall, with blue eyes. Her hair, however, is a dull, darkish brown.

'I don't think I can handle anything that heavy-duty,' Fran says when she comes back to the room. She means the omelette. 'I have to go home in any case. She lives with her mother and her aunt, two women in their mid-seventies, in a drafty farmhouse The farmhouse now has a computer store catty-corner from it. Maya's been to the farm. She's been shown photographs of the way the corner used to be. If land values ever rebound, Fran will be worth millions.

Before Fran leaves she says, 'Has Rab Chatterji called you yet?'

'No.' She remembers the name, a good, reliable Bengali name, from the first night's study of the phone book. Dr Rabindra Chatterji teaches Physics.

'He called the English office just before I left.' She takes car keys out of her pocketbook. She reknots her scarf. 'I bet Indian men are more sensitive than Americans. Rab's a Brahmin, that's what people say.'

A Chatterji has to be a Bengali Brahmin – last names give ancestral secrets away – but Brahminness seems to mean more to Fran than it does to Maya. She was born in 1954, six full years after India became independent. Her India was Nehru's India: a charged, progressive place.

'All Indian men are wife beaters,' Maya says. She means it and doesn't mean it. 'That's why I married an American.' Fran knows about the divorce, but nothing else. Fran is on the Hiring, Tenure, and Reappointment Committee.

Maya sees Fran down the stairs and to the car which is parked in the back in the spot reserved for Maya's car, if she had owned one. It will take her several months to save enough to buy one. She always pays cash, never borrows. She tells herself she's still recovering from the U-Haul drive halfway across the country. Ted Suminski is in his kitchen watching the women. Maya waves to him because waving to him, acknowledging him in that way, makes him seem less creepy. He seems to live alone though a sign, THE SUMINSKIS, hangs from a metal horse's head in the front yard. Maya hasn't seen Mrs Suminski. She hasn't seen any children either. Ted always looks lonely. When she comes back from campus, he's nearly always in the back, throwing darts or shooting baskets.

'What's he like?' Fran gestures with her head as she starts up her car. 'You hear these stories.'

Maya doesn't want to know the stories. She has signed a year's lease. She doesn't want complications. 'He's all right. I keep out of his way.'

'You know what I'm thinking? Of all the people in Cedar Falls, you're the one who could understand Vern best. His wanting to try out his wings, run away, stuff like that.'

'Not really.' Maya is not being modest. Fran is being impulsively democratic, lumping her wayward lover and Indian friend together as headstrong adventurers. For Fran, a utopian and feminist, borders don't count. Maya's taken some big risks, made a break with her parents' ways. She's done things a woman from Ballygunge Park Road doesn't do, even in fantasies. She's not yet shared stories with Fran, apart from the divorce. She's told her nothing of men she picks up, the reputation she'd gained, before Cedar Falls, for 'indiscretions'. She has a job, equity, three friends she can count on for emergencies. She is an American citizen. But.

Fran's Brahmin calls her two nights later. On the phone he presents himself as Dr Chatterji, not Rabindra or Rab. An old-fashioned Indian she assumes. Her father still calls his closest friend 'Colonel.' Dr Chatterji asks her to tea on Sunday. She means to say no but hears herself saying, 'Sunday? Fiveish? I'm not doing anything special this Sunday.'

Outside, Ted Suminski is throwing darts into his garage door. The door has painted-on rings: orange, purple, pink. The bull's-eye is gray. He has to be fifty at least. He is a big, thick, lonely man about whom people tell stories. Maya pulls the phone cord as far as it'll go so she can look down more directly on her landlord's large, bald head. He has his back to her as he lines up a dart. He's in black running shoes, red shorts, he's naked to the waist. He hunches his right shoulder, he pulls the arm back; a big, lonely man shouldn't have so much grace. The dart is ready to cut through the September evening. But Ted Suminski doesn't let go. He swings on worn rubber soles, catches her eye in the window (she has to have imagined this), takes aim at her shadow. Could she have imagined the noise of the dart's metal tip on her windowpane?

Dr Chatterji is still on the phone. 'You are not having any mode of transportation, is that right?'

Ted Suminski has lost interest in her. Perhaps it isn't interest, at all; perhaps it's aggression. 'I don't drive,' she lies, knowing it sounds less shameful than not owning a car. She has said this so often she can get in the right degree of apology and Asian upper-class helplessness. 'It's an awful nuisance.'

'Not to worry, please.' Then, 'It is a great honor to be meeting Dr Sanyal's daughter. In Calcutta business circles he is a legend.'

On Sunday she is ready by 4.30. She doesn't know what the afternoon holds; there are surely no places for 'high tea' – a colonial tradition – in Cedar Falls, Iowa. If he takes her back to his place, it will mean he has invited other guests. From his voice she can tell Dr Chatterji likes to do things correctly. She has dressed herself in a peach-colored nylon georgette sari, jade drop-earrings and a necklace. The color is good on dark skin. She is not pretty, but she does her best. Working at it is a part of self-respect. In the mid-seventies, when American women felt rather strongly about such things, Maya had been in trouble with her women's group at Duke. She was too feminine. She had tried to explain the world she came out of. Her grandmother had been married off at the age of five in a village now in Bangladesh. Her great-aunt had been burned to death over a dowry problem. She herself had been trained to speak softly, arrange flowers, sing, be pliant. If she were to seduce Ted Suminski, she thinks as she waits in the front yard for Dr Chatterji, it would be minor heroism. She has broken with the past. But.

Dr Chatterji drives up for her at about 5.10. He is a hesitant driver. The car stalls, jumps ahead, finally slams to a stop. Maya has to tell him to back off a foot or so; it's hard to leap over two sacks of pruned branches in a sari. Ted Suminski is an obsessive pruner and gardener.

'My sincerest apologies, Mrs Sanyal,' Dr Chatterji says. He leans across the wide front seat of his noisy, very old, very used car and unlocks the door for her. 'I am late. But then, I am sure you're remembering that Indian Standard Time is not at all the same as time in the States.' He laughs. He could be nervous – she often had that effect on Indian men. Or he could just be chatty. 'These Americans are all the time rushing and rushing but where it gets them?' He moves his head laterally once, twice. It's the gesture made famous by Peter Sellers. When Peter Sellers did it, it had seemed hilarious. Now it suggests that Maya and Dr Chatterji have three thousand years plus civilisation, sophistication, moral virtue, over people born on this continent. Like her, Dr Chatterji is a naturalised American.

'Call me Maya,' she says. She fusses with the seat belt. She does it because she needs time to look him over. He seems quite harmless. She takes in the prominent teeth, the eyebrows that run together. He's in a blue shirt and a beige cardigan with the, K-Mart logo that buttons tightly over the waist. It's hard to guess his age because he has dyed his hair and his moustache. Late thirties, early forties. Older than she had expected. 'Not Mrs Sanyal.'

This isn't the time to tell about ex-husbands. She doesn't know where John is these days. He should have kept up at least. John had come into her life as a graduate student at Duke, and she, mistaking the brief breathlessness of sex for love, had married him. They had stayed together two years, maybe a little less. The pain that John had inflicted all those years ago by leaving her had subsided into a cosy feeling of loss. This isn't the time, but then she doesn't want to be a legend's daughter all evening. She's not necessarily on Dr Chatterji's side is what she wants to get across early; she's not against America and Americans. She makes the story – of marriage outside the Brahminic pale, the divorce – quick, dull. Her unsentimentality seems to shock him. His stomach sags inside the cardigan.

'We've each had our several griefs,' the physicist says. 'We're each required to pay our karmic debts.'

'Where are we headed?'

'Mrs Chatterji has made some Indian snacks. She is waiting to meet you because she is knowing your cousin-sister who studied in Scottish Church College. My home is OK, no?'

Fran would get a kick out of this. Maya has slept with married men, with nameless men, with men little more than boys, but never with an Indian man. Never.

The Chatterjis live in a small blue house on a gravelly street. There are at least five or six other houses on the street; the same size but in different colors and with different front yard treatments. More houses are going up. This is the cutting edge of suburbia.

Mrs Chatterji stands in the driveway. She is throwing a large plastic ball to a child. The child looks about four, and is Korean or Cambodian. The child is not hers because she tells it, 'Chung-Hee, ta-ta, bye-bye. Now I play with guest,' as Maya gets out of the car.

Maya hasn't seen this part of town. The early September light softens the construction pits. In that light the houses too close together, the stout woman in a striped cotton sari, the child hugging a pink ball, the two plastic lawn chairs by a tender young tree, the sheets and saris on the clothesline in the back, all seem miraculously incandescent.

'Go home now, Chung-Hee. I am busy.' Mrs Chatterji points the child homeward, then turns to Maya, who has folded her hands in traditional Bengali greeting. 'It is an honor. We feel very privileged.' She leads Maya indoors to a front room that smells of moisture and paint.

In her new, deliquescent mood, Maya allows herself to be backed into the best armchair – a low-backed, boxy Goodwill item draped over with a Rajasthani bedspread – and asks after the cousin Mrs Chatterji knows. She doesn't want to let go of Mrs Chatterji. She doesn't want husband and wife to get into whispered conferences about their guest's misadventures in America, as they make tea in the kitchen.

The coffee table is already laid with platters of mutton croquettes, fish chops, onion pakoras, ghugni with puris, samosas, chutneys. Mrs Chatterji has gone to too much trouble. Maya counts four kinds of sweetmeats in Corning casseroles on an end table. She looks into a see-through lid; spongy, white dumplings float in rosewater syrup. Planets contained, mysteries made visible.

'What are you waiting for, Santana?' Dr Chatterji becomes imperious, though not unaffectionate. He pulls a dining chair up close to the coffee table. 'Make some tea.' He speaks in Bengali to his wife, in English to Maya. To Maya he says, grandly, 'We are having real Indian Green Label Lipton. A nephew is bringing it just one month back.'

His wife ignores him. 'The kettle's already on,' she says. She wants to know about the Sanyal family. Is it true her great-grandfather was a member of the Star Chamber in England?

Nothing in Calcutta is ever lost. Just as her story is known to Bengalis all over America, so are the scandals of her family, the grandfather hauled up for tax evasion, the aunt who left her husband to act in films. This woman brings up the Star Chamber, the glories of the Sanyal family, her father's philanthropies, but it's a way of saying, *I know the dirt.*

The bedrooms are upstairs. In one of those bedrooms an unseen, tormented presence – Maya pictures it as a clumsy ghost that strains to shake off the body's shell – drops things on the floor. The things are heavy and they make the front room's chandelier shake. Light bulbs, shaped like tiny candle flames, flicker. The Chatterjis have said nothing about children. There are no tricycles in the hallway, no small sandals behind the doors.

Maya is too polite to ask about the noise, and the Chatterjis don't explain. They talk just a little louder. They flip the embroidered cover off the stereo. What would Maya like to hear? Hemanta Kumar? Manna Dey? Oh, that young chap, Manna Dey! What sincerity, what tenderness he can convey!

Upstairs the ghost doesn't hear the music of nostalgia. The ghost throws and thumps. The ghost makes its own vehement music. Maya hears in its voice madness, self-hate.

Finally the water in the kettle comes to a boil. The whistle cuts through all fantasy and pretense. Dr Chatterji says, 'I'll see to it,' and rushes out of the room. But he doesn't go to the kitchen. He shouts up the stairwell. 'Poltoo, kindly stop this nonsense straightaway! We're having a brilliant and cultured lady-guest and you're creating earthquakes?' The kettle is hysterical.

Mrs Chatterji wipes her face. The face that had seemed plump and cheery at the start of the evening now is flabby. 'My sister's boy,' the woman says.

So this is the nephew who has brought with him the cartons of Green Label tea, one of which will be given to Maya.

Mrs Chatterji speaks to Maya in English as though only the alien language can keep emotions in check. 'Such an intelligent boy! His father is government servant. Very highly placed.'

Maya is meant to visualise a smart, clean-cut young man from south Calcutta, but all she can see is a crazy, thwarted, lost graduate student. Intelligence, proper family guarantee nothing. Even Brahmins can do self-destructive things, feel unsavory urges. Maya herself had been an excellent student.

'He was First Class First in B. Sc. from Presidency College,' the woman says. 'Now he's getting Master's in Ag. Science at Iowa State.'

The kitchen is silent. Dr Chatterji come back into the room with a tray. The teapot is under a tea cosy, a Kashmiri one embroidered with the usual chinar leaves, loops, and chains. '*Her* nephew,' he says. The dyed hair and dyed moustache are no longer signs of a man wishing to fight the odds. He is a vain man, anxious to cut losses. 'Very unfortunate business.'

The nephew's story comes out slowly, over fish chops and mutton croquettes. He is in love with a student from Ghana. 'Everything was A-OK until the Christmas break. Grades, assistantship for next semester, everything.'

'I blame the college. The office for foreign students arranged a Christmas party. And now, *baapre baap!* Our poor Poltoo wants to marry a Negro Muslim.'

Maya is known for her nasty, ironic one-liners. It has taken her friends weeks to overlook her malicious, un-American pleasure in others' misfortunes. Maya would like to finish Dr Chatterji off quickly. He is pompous; he is reactionary; he wants to live and work in America but give back nothing except taxes. The confused world of the immigrant – the lostness that Maya and Poltoo feel – that's what Dr Chatterji wants to avoid. She hates him. But.

Dr Chatterji's horror is real. A good Brahmin boy in Iowa is in love with an African Muslim. It shouldn't be a big deal. But the more she watches the physicist, the more she realises that 'Brahmin' isn't a caste; it's a metaphor. You break one small rule, and the constellation collapses. She thinks suddenly that John Cheever – she is teaching him as a 'world writer' in her classes, cheek by jowl with Africans and West Indians – would have understood Dr Chatterji's dread. Cheever had been on her mind, ever since the late afternoon light slanted over Mrs Chatterji's drying saris. She remembers now how full of a soft, Cheeverian light Durham had been the summer she had slept with John Hadwen; and how after that, her tidy graduate-student world became monstrous, lawless. All men became John Hadwen; John became all men. Outwardly, she retained her poise, her Brahminical breeding. She treated her crisis as a literary event; she lost her moral sense, her judgment, her power to distinguish. Her parents had behaved magnanimously. They had cabled from Calcutta: WHAT'S DONE IS DONE. WE ARE CONFIDENT YOU WILL HANDLE NEW SITUATIONS WELL. ALL LOVE. But she knows more than do her parents. Love is anarchy.

Poltoo is Mrs Chatterji's favorite nephew. She looks as

though it is her fault that the Sunday has turned unpleasant. She stacks the empty platters methodically. To Maya she says, 'It is the goddess who pulls the strings. We are puppets. I know the goddess will fix it. Poltoo will not marry that African woman.' Then she goes to the coat closet in the hall and staggers back with a harmonium, the kind sold in music stores in Calcutta, and sets it down on the carpeted floor. 'We're nothing but puppets,' she says again. She sits at Maya's feet, her pudgy hands on the harmonium's shiny, black bellows. She sings, beautifully, in a virgin's high voice, 'Come, goddess, come, muse, come to us hapless peoples' rescue.'

Maya is astonished. She has taken singing lessons at Dakshini Academy in Calcutta. She plays the sitar and the tanpur, well enough to please Bengalis, to astonish Americans. But stout Mrs Chatterji is a devotee, talking to God.

A little after eight, Dr Chatterji drops her off. It's been an odd evening and they are both subdued.

'I want to say one thing,' he says. He stops her from undoing her seat belt. The plastic sacks of pruned branches are still at the corner.

'You don't have to get out,' she says.

'Please. Give me one more minute of your time.'

'Sure.'

'Maya is my favorite name.'

She says nothing. She turns away from him without making her embarrassment obvious.

'Truly speaking, it is my favorite. You are sometimes lonely, no? But you are lucky. Divorced women can date, they can go to bars and discos. They can see mens, many mens. But inside marriage there is so much loneliness.' A groan, low, horrible, comes out of him.

She turns back toward him, to unlatch the seat belt and run out of the car. She sees that Dr Chatterji's pants are unzipped. One hand works hard under his Jockey shorts; the other rests, limp, penitential, on the steering wheel.

'Dr Chatterji – *really*!' she cries.

*

The next day, Monday, instead of getting a ride home with Fran – Fran says she *likes* to give rides, she needs the chance to talk, and she won't share gas expenses, absolutely not – Maya goes to the periodicals room of the library. There are newspapers from everywhere, even from Madagascar and New Caledonia. She thinks of the periodicals room as an asylum for homesick aliens. There are two aliens already in the room, both Orientals, both absorbed in the politics and gossip of their far-off homes.

She goes straight to the newspapers from India. She bunches her raincoat like a bolster to make herself more comfortable. There's so much to catch up on. A village headman, a known Congress-Indira party worker, has been shot at by scooter-riding snipers. An Indian pugilist has won an international medal – in Nepal. A child drawing well water – the reporter calls the child 'a neo-Buddhist, a convert from the now-outlawed untouchable caste' – has been stoned. An editorial explains that the story about stoning is not a story about caste but about failed idealism; a story about promises of green fields and clean, potable water broken, a story about bribes paid and wells not dug. But no, thinks Maya, it's about caste.

Out here, in the heartland of the new world, the India of serious newspapers unsettles. Maya longs again to feel what she had felt in the Chatterjis' living room: virtues made physical. It is a familiar feeling, a longing. Had a suitable man presented himself in the reading room at that instant, she would have seduced him. She goes on to the stack of *India Abroad*s, reads through matrimonial columns, and steals an issue to take home.

Indian men want Indian brides. Married Indian men want Indian mistresses. All over America, 'handsome, tall, fair engineers, doctors, data processors – the new pioneers – cry their eerie love calls.

Maya runs a finger down the first column; her fingertip, dark with newsprint, stops at random.

Hello! Hi! Yes, you *are* the one I'm looking for. You are the new emancipated Indo-American woman. You have a zest for life. You are at ease in USA and yet your ethics are rooted in Indian tradition. The man of your dreams has come. Yours truly is handsome, ear-nose-throat specialist, well-settled in Connecticut. Age is 41 but never married, physically fit, sportsmanly, and strong. I adore idealism, poetry, beauty. I abhor smugness, passivity, caste system. Write with recent photo. Better still, call!!!

Maya calls. Hullo, hullo, hullo! She hears immigrant lovers cry in crowded shopping malls. Yes, you who are at ease in both worlds, you are the one. She feels she has a fair chance.

A man answers. 'Ashoke Mehta speaking.'

She speaks quickly into the bright-red mouthpiece of her telephone. He will be in Chicago, in transit, passing through O'Hare. United counter, Saturday, 2 p.m. As easy as that.

'Good,' Ashoke Mehta says. 'For these encounters I, too, prefer a neutral zone.'

On Saturday at exactly two o'clock the man of Maya's dreams floats toward her as lovers used to in shampoo commercials. The United counter is a loud, harassed place but passengers and piled-up luggage fall away from him. Full-cheeked and fleshy-lipped, he is handsome. He hasn't lied. He is serene, assured, a Hindu god touching down in Illinois.

She can't move. She feels ugly and unworthy. Her adult life no longer seems miraculously rebellious; it is grim, it is perverse. She has accomplished nothing. She has changed her citizenship but she hasn't broken through into the light, the vigor, the *hustle* of the New World. She is stuck in dead space.

'Hullo, hullo!' Their fingers touch.

Oh, the excitement! Ashoke Mehta's palm feels so right in the small of her back. Hullo, hullo, hullo. He pushes her out of the reach of anti-Khomeini Iranians, Hare Krishnas, American

Fascists, men with fierce wants, and guides her to an empty gate. They have less than an hour.

'What would you like, Maya?'

She knows he can read her mind, she knows her thoughts are open to him. *You*, she's almost giddy with the thought, with simple desire. 'From the snack bar,' he says, as though to clarify. 'I'm afraid I'm starved.'

Below them, where the light is strong and hurtful, a Boeing is being serviced. 'Nothing,' she says.

He leans forward. She can feel the nap of his scarf – she recognises the Cambridge colors – she can smell the wool of his Icelandic sweater. She runs her hand along the scarf, then against the flesh of his neck. 'Only the impulsive ones call,' he says.

The immigrant courtship proceeds. It's easy, he's good with facts. He knows how to come across to a stranger who may end up a lover, a spouse. He makes over a hundred thousand. He owns a house in Hartford, and two income properties in Newark. He plays the market but he's cautious. He's good at badminton but plays handball to keep in shape. He watches all the sports on television. Last August he visited Copenhagen, Helsinki and Leningrad. Once upon a time he collected stamps but now he doesn't have hobbies, except for reading. He counts himself an intellectual, he spends too much on books. Ludlum, Forsyth, MacInnes; other names she doesn't catch. She suppresses a smile, she's told him only she's a graduate student. He's not without his vices. He's a spender, not a saver. He's a sensualist: good food – all foods, but easy on the Indian – good wine. Some temptations he doesn't try to resist.

And I, she wants to ask, do I tempt?

'Now tell me about yourself, Maya.' He makes it easy for her. 'Have you ever been in love?'

'No.'

'But many have loved you, I can see that.' He says it not unkindly. It is the fate of women like her, and men like him. Their karmic duty, to be loved. It is expected, not judged. She feels he can see them all, the sad parade of need and demand. This isn't the time to reveal all.

And so the courtship enters a second phase.

When she gets back to Cedar Falls, Ted Suminski is standing on the front porch. It's late at night, chilly. He is wearing a down vest. She's never seen him on the porch. In fact there's no chair to sit on. He looks chilled through. He's waited around a while.

'Hi.' She has her keys ready. This isn't the night to offer the six-pack in the fridge. He looks expectant, ready to pounce.

'Hi.' He looks like a man who might have aimed the dart at her. What has he done to his wife, his kids? Why isn't there at least a dog? 'Say, I left a note upstairs.'

The note is written in Magic Marker and thumb-tacked to her apartment door. DUE TO PERSONAL REASONS, NAMELY REMARRIAGE, I REQUEST THAT YOU VACATE MY PLACE AT THE END OF THE SEMESTER.

Maya takes the note down and retacks it to the kitchen wall. The whole wall is like a bulletin board, made of some new, crumbly building material. Her kitchen, Ted Suminski had told her, was once a child's bedroom. Suminski in love: the idea stuns her. She has misread her landlord. The dart at her window speaks of no twisted fantasy. The landlord wants the tenant out.

She gets a glass out of the kitchen cabinet, gets out a tray of ice, pours herself a shot of Fran's bourbon. She is happy for Ted Suminski. She is. She wants to tell someone how moved she'd been by Mrs Chatterji's singing. How she'd felt in O'Hare, even about Dr Rab Chatterji in the car. But Fran is not the person. No one she's ever met is the person. She can't talk about the dead space she lives in. She wishes Ashoke Mehta would call. Right now.

Weeks pass. Then two months. She finds a new room, signs another lease. Her new landlord calls himself Fred. He has no arms, but he helps her move her things. He drives between Ted

Suminski's place and his twice in his station wagon. He uses his toes the way Maya uses her fingers. He likes to do things. He pushes garbage sacks full of Maya's clothes up the stairs.

'It's all right to stare,' Fred says. 'Hell, I would.'

That first afternoon in Fred's rooming house, they share a Chianti. Fred wants to cook her pork chops but he's a little shy about Indians and meat. Is it beef, or pork? Or any meat? She says it's OK, any meat, but not tonight. He has an ex-wife in Des Moines, two kids in Portland, Oregon. The kids are both normal; he's the only freak in the family. But he's self-reliant. He shops in the supermarket like anyone else, he carries out the garbage, shovels the snow off the sidewalk. He needs Maya's help with one thing. Just one thing. The box of Tide is a bit too heavy to manage. Could she get him the giant size every so often and leave it in the basement?

The dead space need not suffocate. Over the months, Fred and she will settle into companionship. She has never slept with a man without arms. Two wounded people, he will joke during their nightly contortions. It will shock her, this assumed equivalence with a man so strikingly deficient. She knows she is strange, and lonely, but being Indian is not the same, she would have thought, as being a freak.

One night in spring, Fred's phone rings. 'Ashoke Mehta speaking.' None of this 'do you remember me?' nonsense. The god has tracked her down. He hasn't forgotten. 'Hullo,' he says, in their special way. And because she doesn't answer back, 'Hullo, hullo, hullo.' She is aware of Fred in the back of the room. He is lighting a cigarette with his toes.

'Yes,' she says, 'I remember.'

'I had to take care of a problem,' Ashoke Mehta says. 'You know that I have my vices. That time at O'Hare I was honest with you.'

She is breathless.

'Who is it, May?' asks Fred.

'You also have a problem,' says the voice. His laugh echoes. 'You will come to Hartford, I know.'

When she moves out, she tells herself, it will not be the end of Fred's world.

Braided Rug

Jane Duran

The all-America rag rug
I hide my feet in
twists as the Hudson
has learned to twist
outdoing its clouds
of dust. It opens out –
as the Missouri offers
in flood and mire
its alms,
or the Potomac pulls
at its raggedy banks.

It braids blue-grey
with river-black, silver
for the rare winter stillness
as if left out all night
by the mountains.
The repeated stopped waters
creak with my weight.

The floorboards of our kitchen
are polished to a nicety.

I am nimble on these knots.
I speak all the riverland tongues
of my mother tongue.
My accent fathers me
My voice is too loud –
even the heron, the herring gull
disappear.

In the middle of London
I am elsewhere. To the long gone,
to the dead in me
I cry breathe now, breathe.
I know my bailiwick.
I stand on my rug.

Checking Out

Mervyn Morris

I slam the door. 'Dear, are you positive
there's nothing left?' Well, no:
something remains, I'm sure of that:

some vestige of our lives in this bare flat
will linger, some impulse will outlive
our going, recycled in the flow

of being. We never leave,
we always have to go.

Biographical Notes

Sujata Bhatt was born in 1956 in Ahmadabad, India and raised in Pune, India. She has lived, studied and worked in the United States and is a graduate of the Writers' Workshop at the University of Iowa. She has published two collections of poetry with Carcanet Press, England and Penguin Books, India: *Brunizem* (1988), which won the Alice Hunt Bartlett Prize and the Commonwealth Poetry Prize (Asia), and *Monkey Shadows* (1991). In spring 1992 she was the Lansdowne Visiting Writer/Professor at the University of Victoria, British Columbia, Canada. She now lives in Bremen with her husband, the German writer Michael Augustin, and their daughter. Sujata Bhatt works as a freelance writer and has translated Gujarati poetry into English for the *Penguin Anthology of Contemporary Indian Women Poets*. Her work has appeared in various British, Irish, American and Canadian journals and her poems have been widely anthologised and have been broadcast on British, German and Dutch Radio. Her new collection *The Stinking Rose* is due from Carcanet in spring 1995.

Fred D'Aguiar was born in London in 1960 and spent his early childhood in Guyana before returning to Britain aged twelve. He trained as a psychiatric nurse before reading English at the University of Kent. His first poetry collection *Mama Dot* (1985) won a Poetry Book Society recommendation. His second, *Airy Hall* (1989) won the Guyana Prize for Poetry. His third poetry collection, *British Subjects* was published in 1993. His poem film *Sweet Thames* (BBC *Words on Film* 1992) won the Race in the

Media Award. His first play, *A Jamaican Airman Foresees his Death* was performed at London's Royal Court Theatre in 1991. Fred D'Aguiar has held the Judith E. Wilson Fellowship at the University of Cambridge and has been a Northern Arts Literary Fellow in Newcastle and Durham. He was a visiting writer at Amherst College, Massachusetts 1992–94 and is now teaching in Florida.

Michael Donoghy was born in New York's South Bronx in 1954 of Irish parents. He attended Fordham University and worked as a doorman in Manhattan. He moved to Chicago in 1977 but after two years abandoned a PhD on Coleridge's *Biographia Literaria* in favour of the sports, blues, art, jazz and poetry scenes. He was poetry editor for the *Chicago Review* for several years and founded the Irish Traditional Band Samhradh Music.

He moved to England in 1985. His first collection, *Shibboleth*, was published in 1988 by Oxford University Press. In 1989 he won the Whitbread Prize for Poetry and the 1989 Geoffrey Faber Prize. His second collection, *Errata* (1993) was selected for the recent New Generation Poets promotion. Michael Donoghy lives in north London, where he plays in several traditional bands and teaches evening classes in the writing of poetry.

Jane Duran was born in Cuba in 1944 and grew up in the USA. She has lived in England since 1966. Her poetry has been published in a number of magazines and anthologies. A pamphlet *Boogie Woogie* was published in 1991 by Hearing Eye and a selection of her work appeared in *Poetry Introduction 8* (Faber and Faber, 1993). Her first collection *Breathe Now, Breathe* is due from Enitharmon Press in 1995.

Michael Hofmann was born in 1957 in Freiburg, Germany and has lived in England since 1961. He studied at Cambridge and has lived in London since 1983. He is the author of three collections of poetry: *Nights in the Iron Hotel*, *Acrimony* and *Corona*, the last of which received a Poetry Book Society Recommendation. He works as an editor and translator and has published a number of translations from the German including Brecht's *The Good Person of Sichuan*, which was performed at the National Theatre in London in 1989.

Aamer Hussein was born in Karachi in 1955 and grew up in Pakistan and India. He has a degree in history and languages from the SOAS, University of London, where he now teaches. A writer since 1987, he is also a highly respected critic and literary translator, contributing to a wide variety of journals and reference books. A critic of international standing, Aamer Hussein has lectured in many countries on comparative literature and reviews regularly for the *Times Literary Supplement*. His fiction has appeared in several journals and anthologies and his work has been published in America, Bangladesh, China, India, Indonesia, Pakistan and the Philippines. His short story collection, *Mirror to the Sun* appeared in 1993 to critical acclaim.

Yasmin Issacs was born in Jamaica in 1959 and grew up there and in England. She has been writing poetry for most of her adult life.

Kelvin Christopher James was born in the Caribbean island of Trinidad and attended the University of the West Indies at St Augustine, before moving to the USA. He received his Master's degree in education from Columbia University. In 1989 he won a New York Foundation for the Arts Fellowship. *Jumping Ship* (1992), his collection of short stories, weaves together the voices of both the Caribbean and urban North America. Both this and his novel *Secrets* (1993) have received widespread praise. Kelvin Christopher James has made his home in Harlem.

Mimi Khalvati was born in Tehran in 1944 and educated in England. She worked as an actress and director at the Theatre Workshop in Tehran and translated extensively from English to Farsi as well as devising new plays. While bringing up two children she co-founded the Theatre in Exile group, directed plays on the fringe and published a children's book *I Know A Place* (Dent, 1985). Her poetry has been widely anthologised, featuring in *Anvil New Poets* (1990), *New Women Poets* (Bloodaxe, 1993), *The Forward Book of Poetry* (1993 and 1995). She has published a pamphlet collection, *Persian Miniatures* (Smith Doorstop, 1990). Her first full collection of poems *In White Ink* (Carcanet) was published in 1991 to wide acclaim. Her most recent collection *Mirrorworks* (Carcanet, 1995) has been equally well received.

Adam Lively was born in Swansea and studied history and philosophy in England and America. He is the author of four novels: *Blue Fruit* (1988), *The Burnt House* (1989), *The Snail* (1991) and *Sing the Body Electric* (1993) and was selected as one of the Best of Young British Novelists in 1993. His four novels successfully cross many of the accepted norms of literary mores. Adam Lively lives in London with his wife and two small children.

Sindiwe Magona grew up in Transkei village and on the Cape Flats. She worked as a teacher and a domestic in South Africa before obtaining degrees from the University of London and UNISA. She obtained a bursary to study at the Columbia School of Social Work in New York. Later she joined the United Nations, working in radio at the Department of Public Information. She is the author of a two-part autobiography, *To My Children's Children* (1991) and *Forced to Grow* (1992) and a collection of short stories, *Living, Loving and Lying Awake at Nights* (1992) all published by the Women's Press. She lives in New York with her children.

Mervyn Morris was born in Jamaica in 1937. After graduating from the University of the West Indies, he read English at St Edmund Hall, Oxford. Mervyn lives in Jamaica and is currently a Reader in West Indian Literature at the University of the West Indies. His poetry collections include *The Pond* (1973), *Shadowboxing* (1979) and *Examination Centre* (1992) all published by New Beacon. As an academic Mervyn has published many articles. He has also prepared several anthologies, including *Voiceprint* (1989) (with Stewart Brown and Gordon Rohiehr) and *The Faber Book of Contemporary Caribbean Short Stories* (1990). In 1992 he was a UK Arts Council visiting writer in residence at the South Bank Centre in London.

Bharati Mukherjee is the author of three novels, *Wife*, *The Tiger's Daughter* and *Jasmine*, two works of non-fiction *Days and Nights in Calcutta* and *The Sorrow and the Terror* and two collections of short stories *Darkness* and *Middleman and Other Stories*. Born and educated in Calcutta, she has studied and taught in the USA, where she now lives. In 1989 she became the first naturalised American to win the National Book Circle Critics Award.

Joan Riley was born in Jamaica and studied in England. She has degrees in international relations, applied social studies and politics from the Universities of Sussex and London. She is the author of four novels: *The Unbelonging* (1985), *Waiting in the Twilight* (1987), *Romance* (1988) and *A Kindness to the Children* (1992). Her work has been dramatised for both radio and television. Her fiction and non-fiction have been widely anthologised in English and in translation in Europe, Africa and the Americas. Her short stories have appeared in a number of publications, including *Storia I* (Pandora, 1988), *Her True True Name* (Heinemann, 1989), *Us/Them* (Rudopi, 1991), *Daughters of Africa* (Cape, 1992), *Black Star* (1993) and *Inside Ant's Belly* (Nate, 1994). In the past she has taught literature and creative writing and reviewed for a number of publications, including *Africa Concord, New Socialist* and the BBC World Service. She is currently working on a collection of short stories and a new novel.

Hanan Al Shayk is one of the foremost contemporary writers in Arabic. Born in Lebanon and brought up in Beirut, she received her education in Cairo. She was a successful journalist in Beirut, later moving to live in the Arabian Gulf. She has lived in London with her husband and two children since 1982, largely as a result of the civil war in Lebanon. Hanan Al Shayk is the author of five novels and two collections of short stories. Three of her novels have been widely translated from their original Arabic. The highly acclaimed *Women of Sand and Myrrh* was one of the *Publishers Weekly* (New York) fifty best books of 1992. It was amongst the Feminist Book Festival's top ten titles in 1993 and won the *ELLE* literary prize for the Bourgogne France. Her other two novels available in translation are *The Story of Zahra* and *Beirut Blues* (Chatto and Windus 1995).

Hanan Al Shayk's translator, Catherine Cobham, teaches modern Arabic literature at the University of St Andrews.

Jan Lo Shinebourne was born and grew up in Guyana. She now lives in London. Her first novel, *Timepiece* (Peepal Tree Press, Leeds 1986) won the Guyana Prize for a first novel (1987). Her second novel is *The Last English Plantation* (Peepal Tree Press, 1988). Her short stories have been widely anthologised and have appeared in several journals including *Best West Indian Stories* (1982), *Her True-True Name* (1989), *Caribbean New Wave* (1990), *Kyk-Over-Al (Georgetown Guyana), Trinidad & Tobago Review* (Port of Spain, Trinidad) *Wasafari* and *Everywoman*. She is also a critic and essayist, with articles in *Spare Rib*, *Race Today*, *Southall Review*, *New Beacon Review* and the *Saturday Times Review*.

Forthcoming writing will include a work of fiction, chapters in three academic publications and an essay in *Zones-*

X-ing: Photographs and Essays on the Borders (New Press, New York, 1996).

Bapsi Sidhwe was born in Karachi and brought up in Lahore. A member of the Zoroastrian community, she writes from a unique perspective and enjoys the reputation as Pakistan's finest English-language novelist. She divides her time between the USA, where she teaches, and Pakistan.

Pierre Tran was born in Vietnam and taken to England by his parents at the height of the Vietnam war. Educated at Sussex University, he started work in public relations before moving full time to journalism. He has worked for the *Economist* and spent a number of years in France. He has worked for Reuters for many years and is currently on posting in Paris.

Briar Wood was born in New Zealand and grew up in Auckland City. She studied at the University of Auckland and taught high school in the King Country area. She came to Britain in 1983 and has worked as a teacher, critic, editor and writer. For two years she edited the poetry section of the London Listings magazine *City Limits*. She has a D. Phil. from Sussex University and worked as a lecturer in new literatures in English, women's studies and creative writing at the University of North London. She returned to New Zealand in February 1994 to take up a two-year post-doctoral post at Auckland University. Her poetry has been published in newspapers, magazines and periodicals, including *Landfall.* A selection of her poems was published in *New Women Poets* (Bloodaxe) and *Virago New Poets* (Virago).

Zinovy Zinik was born in 1945 in Moscow. After studying topology at Moscow University, he began writing prose in the mid-1960s, becoming a contributor to the magazine *Theatre*. In 1975 Zinik emigrated to Israel, and directed a Russian-language theatre group at Jerusalem's Hebrew University. At the end of 1976 he was invited to London to work for the BBC Russian

Service. Since the 1980s Zinik has worked as a freelance critic and lecturer, and remains editor of *West End*, the BBC Russian Service's arts magazine. He is also a regular contributor to *The Times Literary Supplement* in London.

Zinovy Zinik's six novels, written since his departure from Russia, all examine aspects of the duality and duplicity of *émigré* existence – with its clash of East and West, past and present. Zinik was the first of the writers of the 'third wave' of emigration from the Soviet Union to set their work in the Western world. Originally written in Russian, his novels *A Displaced Person* (1977) and *A Niche in the Pantheon* (1979) first appeared in French translation. *Russian Service* (1981) was also adapted for BBC Radio 3 and Radio France. *The Mushroom Picker* was published in 1986 in English; it was dramatised for BBC2 television in 1993. His novel *The Lord and the Gamekeeper* (1989) has also been published in English. Apart from English and French, Zinik's work has been translated into Hebrew, Dutch, Polish, Hungarian and Estonian. Russian editions of his novels have now appeared, after more than sixteen years during which his work was banned in the Soviet Union.

Now a British citizen, Zinovy Zinik lives in London with his wife Nina; he has two children.

THE VIRAGO BOOK OF WOMEN TRAVELLERS

Edited by Mary Morris and Larry O'Connor

'An excellent collection' – *Sunday Times*

'A volume in which rich and unexpected seams of precious minerals await discovery' – *Guardian*

'From the acerbic wit of Freya Stark to the raw courage of Dervla Murphy, over three hundred years of the best and bravest women's travel writing is gathered here in a collection of stunning journeys we can all take – on the page and in the imagination' – *The List*

Three hundred years of wanderlust are captured here as women travel for peril and pleasure, whether to gaze into Persian gardens or imbibe the French countryside, to challenge to fierce Sahara or climb an impossible mountain.

THE COLOUR OF FORGETTING

Merle Collins

'A novel that conjures up magical, luminous stories and seamlessly weaves together history and memory'
Margaret Busby

'From the subversively and hilariously satirical to the impassioned . . . Collins draws on story-telling techniques, choruses and echoes which come from her mother, grandmother and the community as a whole'
Guardian

Merle Collins' profoundly lyrical new novel is an exquisite tribute to the Caribbean, past and present. Set on the mythical islands of Paz and Eden, this is a story of everyday triumphs and heartbreaks. Land disputes, family feuds, political upheaval and personal trauma shake the inhabitants as the modern encroaches on the ancient. And through it all Carib, sensitive to the whispering spirits, labelled crazy by the islanders, instructs the boy Thunder to manhood through the story of his chequered ancestry.

NO PLACE LIKE HOME

Yasmin Alibhai-Brown

'A brave and unflinchingly honest book"
Meera Syal

'Although this book has enough political content to be a valuable historical document, it is as a memoir that it cuts deepest'
Daily Telegraph

'A candid and far from bitter account of life as an outsider'
Independent

Yasmin Alibhai-Brown's vivid and fiercely moving account of life for Asians in Uganda where resentments, fear and paranoia ran high for the Asian community, during Idi Amin's reign of terror.

WHOLE OF A MORNING SKY

Grace Nichols

'Nichols has wit, acidity, tenderness, any number of gifts at her disposal . . . She has the discipline of a poet; there are no wasted words or excessive descriptions, but a sure sense of what is sufficient'
Jeanette Winterson

'There's real art in her accumulation of ordinary detail . . . a clear, lyrical, unforced style'
Observer

Along with the sweep of political upheavals – strikes, riots and racial clashes – daily life in the Walcott's Charleston neighbourhood and beyond gathers its own intensity. Grace Nichols richly and imaginatively evokes her Guyanese childhood in this, her first adult novel.